Low-sodium Cookbook

Low-sodium Cookbook

Jenny Salmon

HAMLYN
London · New York · Sydney · Toronto

The following titles are also available in this series:
Arthritic Cookbook · Diabetic Cookbook
Low Fat Cookbook

Front cover
and inside photography by David Johnson
Illustrations by Jo Lawrence

Published in 1984 by
The Hamlyn Publishing Group Limited
London · New York · Sydney · Toronto
Astronaut House, Feltham, Middlesex, England
© Copyright The Hamlyn Publishing Group Limited 1984

ISBN 0 600 32407 9

Set in Monophoto Sabon
by Servis Filmsetting Limited, Manchester
Printed in Yugoslavia

Contents

Useful Facts and Figures

Notes on metrication

Exact conversion from Imperial to metric measures does not usually give very convenient working quantities and so the metric measures have been rounded off into units of 25 grams. The table below shows the recommended equivalents for solid and liquid measures.

Ounces	Approx g to nearest whole figure	Recommended conversion to nearest unit of 25	Ounces	Approx g to nearest whole figure	Recommended conversion to nearest unit of 25
1	28	25	6	170	175
2	57	50	7	198	200
3	85	75	8	227	225
4	113	100	9	255	250
5	142	150	10	283	275

Note: When converting quantities over 20 oz first add the appropriate figures in the centre column, then adjust to the nearest unit of 25. As a general guide, 1 kg (1000 g) equals 2.2 lb or about 2 lb 3 oz. This method of conversion gives good results in nearly all cases, although in certain pastry and cake recipes a more accurate conversion is necessary to produce a balanced recipe.

Spoon measures All spoon measures given in this book are level unless otherwise stated.

Imperial	Approx ml to nearest whole figure	Recommended ml	Imperial	Approx ml to nearest whole figure	Recommended ml
$\frac{1}{4}$ pint	142	150ml	1 pint	567	600ml
$\frac{1}{2}$ pint	283	300ml	$1\frac{1}{2}$ pints	851	900ml
$\frac{3}{4}$ pint	425	450ml	$1\frac{3}{4}$ pints	992	1000ml (1 litre)

Oven temperatures The table below gives recommended equivalents.

	°C	°F	Gas Mark		°C	°F	Gas Mark
Very cool	110	225	$\frac{1}{4}$	Moderately hot	190	375	5
	120	250	$\frac{1}{2}$		200	400	6
Cool	140	275	1	Hot	220	425	7
	150	300	2		230	450	8
Moderate	160	325	3	Very hot	240	475	9
	180	350	4				

Notes for American and Australian users

In America the 8-fl oz measuring cup is used. In Australia metric measures are now used in conjunction with the standard 250-ml measuring cup. The Imperial pint, used in Britain and Australia, is 20 fl oz, while the American pint is 16 fl oz. The British standard tablespoon, which has been used throughout this book, holds 17.7 ml, the American 14.2 ml, and the Australian 20 ml. A teaspoon holds approximately 5 ml in all three countries.

British	American	Australian	British	American	Australian
1 teaspoon	1 teaspoon	1 teaspoon	$3\frac{1}{2}$ tablespoons	4 tablespoons	3 tablespoons
1 tablespoon	1 tablespoon	1 tablespoon	4 tablespoons	5 tablespoons	$3\frac{1}{2}$ tablespoons
2 tablespoons	3 tablespoons	2 tablespoons			

An Imperial/American guide to liquid measures

Imperial	American	Imperial	American
$\frac{1}{4}$ pint	$\frac{2}{3}$ cup	1 pint	$2\frac{1}{2}$ cups
$\frac{1}{2}$ pint	$1\frac{1}{4}$ cups	$1\frac{1}{2}$ pints	$3\frac{3}{4}$ cups
$\frac{3}{4}$ pint	2 cups	2 pints	5 cups ($2\frac{1}{2}$ pints)

Note: When making any of the recipes in this book, only follow one set of measures as they are not interchangeable.

Introduction

A low-sodium diet isn't just for people who are very ill with kidney problems or very high blood pressure: it's for everyone who cares about good health and good food. There is no doubt that, as a nation, we eat far more sodium – mainly as salt – than we need to be healthy. The real question is, does this excess matter and does it do any harm?

A relatively few people need a diet that contains a very small amount of sodium because they have certain liver or kidney disorders, or water retention caused by a specific form of heart disease. But there are a great many more who have high blood pressure and who are therefore advised to cut their salt intake dramatically. Antihypertensive drugs are very effective in lowering high blood pressure but many people would rather find simpler forms of treatment if they can, and they are willing to begin by changing their diets. Quite apart from those people who already have high blood pressure, many more could reduce the risk of getting high blood pressure if they eat less salt while they are young and still healthy.

This book is written mainly for people who acknowledge that they don't *need* a high-salt diet and that their health could benefit in the long term by reducing their salt intake. It's also for people who want food that tastes good. Most of the recipes have a very low fat content too, and they are also calorie counted because being overweight is as bad for blood pressure as eating too much salt. People with liver, kidney or heart disorders may find the recipes suitable for their diets, but they may need to modify other diet components too. The advice of a dietitian or doctor should be sought to assess whether the recipes are indeed suitable for specific medical complaints.

Salt or Sodium?

The words 'salt' and 'sodium' are often used indiscriminately and interchangeably. In fact, they are two different substances. The salt we add to cooking and shake on food is sodium chloride which is made up of almost equal amounts of sodium and chloride. The difference between sodium and salt become important when you start thinking about the amount of sodium or salt you should be eating each day. Sodium makes up 40% of the weight of salt, so if a food contains 0.3 g (or 300 mg) of sodium, that's the same as saying it has 0.75 g (or 750 mg) salt. When you read any figures for the amount of salt or sodium in different foods, be sure you know which they refer to.

As far as health is concerned, the current medical view is that we need to be careful about the amount of sodium we eat. It's true that most of our sodium does come from salt, but there is some in monosodium glutamate, a flavour enhancer used by the food industry, and some in baking powder and other raising agents. It's also important to remember that sauces like soy and Worcestershire contain quite large amounts of sodium.

In this book quantities of sodium are referred to in milligrams rather than grams.

The Case For Sodium

There's absolutely no doubt that we all need to eat some sodium – it helps to keep the body's fluid balance right by making sure that the correct amounts of water are inside body cells as well as in the fluid that surrounds them. Sodium is also important in maintaining blood pressure (too little means the pressure falls dangerously low), for the efficient functioning of muscles and for the transmission of nerve impulses to and from the brain.

The amount that's needed to fulfil these functions is about 200 mg sodium (equivalent to 500 mg salt) a day. People who regularly loose large amounts of sweat – for example athletes and steel furnace workers – may need slightly more. On average, we eat twenty times that amount.

The Case Against Sodium

There is, as yet, no absolute proof that a high-sodium diet inevitably and universally leads to high blood pressure. Some people, because of the genes they inherited, may be immune to the effect of a high sodium intake. No matter how much salt they add to foods they won't get high blood pressure. But for many others, who are genetically susceptible, studies have

8

shown a link between hypertension (high blood pressure) and diet. Much of the evidence incriminating sodium comes from looking at people in different countries, their diets and levels of blood pressure. By and large, the more salt the community eats, the more likely they are to have a large number of people with high blood pressure. There are countries which don't fit into the pattern, but many health authorities advise us to cut sodium intake. After all, we certainly don't *need* the amount we currently eat, and cutting down may do some good.

It is even more important that children should not get accustomed to eating large amounts of salty foods. Some research indicates that a high-salt diet in infancy and early childhood may predispose the individual to high blood pressure later in adult life. And there is no doubt that the taste for salty food is acquired – so getting used to the taste of unsalted, or lightly seasoned, foods in childhood is a good idea.

When it comes to high blood pressure, body weight is just as important as sodium intake. The first thing most doctors recommend to a hypertensive, overweight patient is to reduce body weight to normal. Very often this alone will bring blood pressure down to normal or near-normal. A low-sodium diet will also help. All recipes are calorie counted so that you can monitor your calorie intake and adjust it if necessary, to lose weight if you need to.

How Much Sodium?

It's not easy to measure the amount of sodium we actually eat because a large proportion of it comes from the salt sprinkled on food at the dining table. It is, however, relatively easy to measure the amount of sodium obtained from the food itself. Current estimates suggest that we get 3,200 mg sodium (8,000 mg salt) from food, and table salt could supply an additional 1,200 mg sodium (3,000 mg salt) a day. Compare that with the 200 mg sodium we actually need!

There is no doubt that some people eat less than the average, and some a great deal more. But, even so, the current average intake is twenty times the amount we need. Theoretically, it is possible to cut our sodium intake to the 200 mg we need. In practice, such a dramatic reduction would be extremely difficult because the food would seem totally unpalatable to most people. Fortunately, there seems little advantage in reducing the sodium intake below about 2,000 to 2,500 mg a day, and even that means halving the present intake.

Sources of Sodium

Used in cooking food at home, with vegetables and sprinkled on food at the table, table salt is a major source of sodium in the average British diet. Among bought foods, bread provides more sodium than any other group. In the following table, figures for meat, fish and vegetables refer to the natural food, without any added salt.

FOODS THAT CONTRIBUTE TO SODIUM
INTAKE IN THE AVERAGE UK DIET

	mg sodium/day
table salt	1,200
bread	1,300
meat, eggs and meat products	700
butter and cheese	400
milk, fish, fruit and vegetables	800
Total	4,400

Therefore, it might seem that the best way to reduce sodium intake would be cut down on the amount of bread eaten and to eliminate all added salt. That would halve sodium intake – which is what we are being asked to do by the health authorities – but that is not sensible. Bread is an extremely valuable food, not only because it contains many useful nutrients and dietary fibre, but also because so many people rely on it to make sandwiches for at least one meal a day. Above all, people like bread.

Palatability

Cutting salt intake is important, but it's equally important to make sure that your diet in general is a healthy one. That means eating plenty of fruits and vegetables, only a little sugar-rich food and adequate amounts of cereals like bread. Equally as important is making sure the healthy diet tastes good. If you don't like your healthy food you won't eat it!

So, just cutting out bread is not a healthy option. You can make your own bread without salt, at first it may taste strange, but you will get used to the flavour. However, home-made breads can be flavoured with herbs, spices and other well-flavoured ingredients.

Let's assume that ordinary bread is going to stay in your healthy low-sodium diet. That means something else has to go: the obvious ingredient is table salt and cooking salt, and that's not difficult. Have you ever looked at people in a restaurant – or even in your own home – and seen how many of them sprinkle salt all over their food before they even taste it? It's bad for their health, and more than a little insulting to the cook who has probably taken great pains to get the flavour balance just right.

There is no doubt that, as children, we develop a taste for salty foods which means that we go on wanting more and more salt. But that doesn't happen overnight. Equally, it is possible, over a period of time, to get used to using far less salt in cooking and on food. Like all change, cutting down on your salt intake is much more likely to be successful in the long term if you go about it slowly. If you normally shake salt all over food, start by pouring just a small amount on the side of the plate instead, then use less in cooking meats and fish, then less with vegetables and so on. At the same time, get used to substituting herbs and spices for plain salt.

Eating What You Like

Even on a low-sodium diet, you are allowed some sodium. As long as you know what you are doing, you can choose how you eat your daily allowance. It really depends on your personal preference. Some people are very happy with no salt in meat and fish dishes but can't eat a boiled egg without a pinch of salt; for others chips without salt are not worth eating. On the other hand some people could not imagine life without bacon, a food which contains a large amount of sodium. Providing you don't eat bacon, chips and boiled eggs with salt every day, you'll be able to eat some foods with a little salt and still keep your sodium intake down.

Some Surprising Sources of Sodium

Almost all prepared or convenience foods contain sodium, not only in the form of salt but also as monosodium glutamate (MSG) in savoury foods. Looking at most food labels won't help you find out the sodium content because there is no obligation on food producers to state the sodium or salt contents of the product. Here are just a few examples to illustrate how much sodium some foods contain. A more extensive list of foods and their sodium contents is given in the charts at the end of this chapter. Remember that you are aiming for a total daily intake of 2,000 to 2,500 mg of sodium.

	Sodium Content (in mg)
300 ml/½ pt canned soup	1,300
75 g/3 oz cooked peeled prawns	1,200
2 large sausages	870
150 g/5 oz canned baked beans	720
2 (50-g/2-oz) beef burgers	690
75-g/3-oz slice veal and ham pie	620
25 g/1 oz sweet pickle	500
25 g/1 oz All Bran	400

If you stop to think about the way different foods are made, you won't be surprised at the high sodium content of some of them. Cheese, for example, has salt added, but not the same amount in all kinds of cheese. The saltiest cheeses are Camembert, Danish Blue and Stilton. A 50-g/2-oz piece of any of these will contain 500 to 600 mg sodium. Cheddar is not quite so high, and cottage or cream cheeses are lowest of all.

When you want to add flavour to a meat dish but don't want to pour in salt, you may be tempted to reach for the Worcestershire sauce bottle. A dash or two is fine, but a few tablespoons is not: 1 tablespoon contains 200 mg sodium. Similarly, stock cubes are mainly salt; one cube might contain up to 1,000 mg sodium. Some breakfast cereals have added salt, others don't. Among the ones which contain the most sodium are All Bran, Cornflakes and Rice Krispies. Cereals with no added salt are Puffed Wheat and Shredded Wheat.

Self-raising flour, as you buy it, contains about 100 mg sodium in each ounce and the raising agent in scones means that a 50-g/2-oz scone can contain up to 400 mg sodium. If you want to save on sodium, but go on eating these, you can make up your own raising agent and add it to plain flour. The mixture is on page 116 and the ingredients can be obtained from the pharmacist.

Butter may not taste salty, but it too contains about 230 mg sodium in each 25 g/1 oz. Unsalted butter is readily available and many people prefer it to the salted variety.

Herbs and Spices

There's no doubt that salt and salty ingredients, like bacon, do add to the overall flavour of meat and fish dishes. But they are by no means essential in all of them. There are so many herbs and spices which are very easy to find in supermarkets and markets and they give the most wonderful flavour to foods. Fresh herbs are usually better than dried ones and the majority are easy to grow at home, even if you have only a window box or a few flower pots on the kitchen sill. Parsley, sage and thyme are very easy to grow and, if you have more room, try rosemary and all the different kinds of mint. A bay tree is a pretty expensive item, but it is worth asking for one as a present.

A few basic spices to keep in stock are nutmeg, cinnamon, cumin, coriander and whole cloves. Spices are better if they are freshly ground at home, but the powdered varieties are a good second best. You can have great fun combining different spices to make Indian dishes.

Using This Book

The sodium content of the recipes is cut to an absolute minimum, but remember that you can have up to 2,500 mg of sodium a day. By using the table of sodium contents you can work out what you're likely to be eating from milk, bread and other foods which may not be very low in salt but which you don't want to give up.

You could add salt to these recipes, but remember that each level teaspoon contains 2,000 mg of sodium. If the recipe serves four portions, each one will contain 500 mg sodium. It's sensible to find out which foods and dishes you really need to add salt or salty foods to, then calculate the sodium content. There is bound to be a way to use your salt allowance so that your sodium intake is still at a minimum but so that you can still eat flavourful foods. Read through the following notes and ingredients before attempting the recipes.

Butter: Unsalted butter is used because it is much easier to find than unsalted margarine. Corn oil can be used for frying.

Tomato purée: Use a variety which does not contain salt or sodium-containing ingredients. Look at the labels to see whether salt is one of the components.

Flour: All flour used in these recipes is plain. Make your own low-sodium self-raising flour by following the instructions on page 116.

Vegetables: Try to get used to cooking vegetables without adding any salt; similarly rice and pasta. This may not be easy, and if you decide you just can't eat unsalted vegetables, use the following chart to calculate the rough sodium intake from these foods:

	Sodium mg/100g (4oz)
Vegetables, lightly salted	100
Vegetables, heavily salted	300
Rice and pasta, lightly salted	100
Rice and pasta, heavily salted	500

Lightly salted means adding a small pinch of salt to each 300 ml/½ pint cooking water. Heavily salted indicates that 1 level teaspoon salt is added to each 300 ml/½ pint water. Canned vegetables contain about 250 to 300 mg sodium per 100 g/4 oz portion. Some vegetables canned in plain water are now on the market.

Sodium and Calorie Values of Some Foods

(All vegetables are boiled without salt)

	Quantity	Sodium (mg)	Calories
All Bran	50 g/2 oz	830	140
Apple (1 average)	125 g/4½ oz	3	50
Avocado pear	100 g/4 oz	5	160
Bacon, grilled	25 g/1 oz	400	85
Baked beans	150 g/5 oz	720	100
Banana (1 small)	125 g/4½ oz	1	60
Beans, broad	50 g/2 oz	10	30
Beef, roast lean	50 g/2 oz	30	180
Beefburgers, grilled (1 small)	50 g/2 oz	350	130
Beer	300 ml/½ pint	40	90
Biscuits:			
digestive (1 biscuit)	15 g/½ oz	65	70
shortbread (1 biscuit)	25 g/1 oz	65	125
water (1 biscuit)	25 g/1 oz	120	110
Bovril	1 teaspoon	240	10
Brazil nuts (6)	25 g/1 oz	1	150
Bread: white (1 medium–thick slice)	40 g/1½ oz	180	95
wholemeal (1 medium–thick slice)	40 g/1½ oz	220	85
Butter	1 teaspoon	40	40
Cabbage, boiled	50 g/2 oz	4	10
Carrots, boiled	50 g/2 oz	20	10
Cake, gingerbread (1 slice)	35 g/1½ oz	75	130
Cauliflower, boiled	50 g/2 oz	4	10
Cheese:			
Cheddar	50 g/2 oz	300	200
Danish blue	50 g/2 oz	710	180
Edam	50 g/2 oz	490	150
Stilton	50 g/2 oz	575	230
cottage	50 g/2 oz	250	55
cream	30 g/1 oz	90	130
Chicken, roast	50 g/2 oz	40	75
Chocolate, milk (small bar)	50 g/2 oz	60	270
Coconut, desiccated	3 tablespoons	5	90

Cod, poached			
or grilled	100 g/4 oz	80	95
Corned beef	50 g/2 oz	480	110
Cornflakes	20 g/1 oz	230	75
Crab meat	50 g/2 oz	140	60
Cream:			
double	2 tablespoons	8	130
single	2 tablespoons	12	60
Dates	25 g/1 oz	1	65
Duck, roast lean	50 g/2 oz	50	100
Egg, boiled or poached (1)	60 g/2¼ oz	80	90
Fish fingers, grilled (2)	60 g/2¼ oz	190	110
Flour:			
plain	2 tablespoons	0	65
self-raising	2 tablespoons	70	65
Gammon (lean), boiled	50 g/2 oz	550	80
Gin	1 single measure	0	55
Grapefruit (¼ large)	75 g/3 oz	1	15
Grapes	50 g/2 oz	1	35
Haddock, poached			
or grilled	100 g/4 oz	80	95
Herring, grilled	100 g/4 oz	170	200
Honey	1 tablespoon	2	45
Ice cream	75 g/3 oz	60	120
Jam	1 tablespoon	3	40
Jelly (made up)	150 ml/¼ pint	8	85
Kidney (lamb's), stewed	50 g/2 oz	110	45
Kippers	50 g/2 oz	500	100
Lamb (lean), roast	50 g/2 oz	30	80
Leeks, boiled	100 g/4 oz	6	30
Liver, grilled	50 g/2 oz	80	75
Liver pâté	50 g/2 oz	430	160
Luncheon meat	50 g/2 oz	525	160
Macaroni, boiled	100 g/4 oz	8	110
Mackerel, grilled	125 g/4½ oz	150	280
Margarine	1 teaspoon	40	40
Marmalade	1 tablespoon	3	40
Marmite	1 teaspoon	225	10
Melon	150 g/5 oz	20	30
Milk:			
whole	300 ml/½ pint	140	190
skimmed	300 ml/½ pint	140	100
evaporated	1 tablespoon	30	25

Oatmeal, raw	1 heaped tablespoon	1	20
Olives (5)	25 g/1 oz	560	25
Orange (1 small)	100 g/1 oz	3	35
Orange juice	150 ml/¼ pint	4	50
Parsnip, boiled	100 g/4 oz	5	60
Peach (1 average)	100 g/4 oz	5	35
Peanuts, salted	25 g/1 oz	110	140
Peanut butter	1 tablespoon	55	90
Peas	2 heaped tablespoons	2	20
Pilchards, canned in tomato sauce (1 average)	25 g/1 oz	95	30
Pineapple canned (1 ring)	75 g/3 oz	2	35
Plaice, grilled	100 g/4 oz	120	100
Pork, roast lean	50 g/2 oz	40	95
Potato, boiled (1 medium)	175 g/6 oz	10	150
Potato crisps, salted (1 small packet)	25 g/1 oz	140	130
Prawns, cooked and peeled	25 g/1 oz	400	30
Prunes (5), soaked	40 g/1½ oz	5	30
Puffed wheat	25 g/1 oz	1	80
Raisins	1 heaped tablespoon	10	60
Raspberries	75 g/3 oz	4	15
Rice, boiled	50 g/2 oz	1	60
Rice Krispies	6 heaped tablespoons	220	95
Salmon:			
poached	110 g/4 oz	110	225
canned	50 g/2 oz	300	90
Salt	1 level teaspoon	2,000	0
Sardines, canned in tomato sauce	25 g/1 oz	175	45
Sausages (1 large), grilled	40 g/1½ oz	430	120
Salami (3 thin slices)	25 g/1 oz	460	120
Shredded Wheat (1)	28 g/1 oz	2	90
Soup:			
canned tomato	300 ml/½ pint	1,300	160
dried tomato	300 ml/½ pint	1,100	90
Spinach, boiled	120 g/4½ oz	140	35
Sweetcorn: frozen, boiled	25 g/1 oz	1	30
canned in brine	15 g/½ oz	80	30

Syrup, golden	1 tablespoon	40	50
Tomato (1 average)	50 g/2 oz	1	10
Tomato purée:			
without salt	1 tablespoon	4	15
with salt	1 tablespoon	65	15
Tongue, canned	50 g/2 oz	520	100
Trout: fresh water,			
grilled	125 g/4½ oz	110	170
sea water, grilled	125 g/4½ oz	260	170
Tuna, canned in oil	50 g/2 oz	210	145
Veal (1 escalop), fried	75 g/3 oz	100	170
Walnuts (10 halves)	25 g/1 oz	1	130
Weetabix (1)	20 g/½ oz	70	60
Yogurt: (individual cartons)			
plain:	150 ml/¼ pint	110	70
fruit:	150 ml/¼ pint	90	140

Soups and Stocks

Most canned and dried soups are extremely salty and they usually contain monosodium glutamate which adds to the total sodium content. In addition to being low in sodium, home-made soups can also have a full flavour derived from herbs and spices and the lack of salt can be disguised by using unusual ingredients such as oranges and other fruits.

Stocks are the basis of so many soups, savoury sauces and casseroles that it's difficult to imagine life without conventional stock cubes. But a little thought and effort will make you realise just how easy it is to make your own stocks. If you boil the stock well to evaporate a large proportion of the water, you'll be able to freeze the concentrate; but remember to dilute it before use!

Court Bouillon

Per recipe: 50 mg sodium   40 calories

900 ml/1½ pints water
1 carrot, sliced
1 medium onion, sliced
3 cloves
bouquet garni (below)
6 peppercorns
2 tablespoons vinegar or white wine

Place all the ingredients in a large saucepan and bring to the boil, then reduce the heat and cover the pan. Simmer gently for 15 minutes. Strain the court bouillon and use as required. **Makes about 900 ml/1½ pints**

Bouquet Garni

Per portion: nil mg sodium   nil calories

1 clove
3 peppercorns
generous pinch of thyme
bay leaf
blade of mace
chopped parsley, rosemary or basil

Make several bouquet garni at the same time, if you like, and store them in an airtight jar. Place the herbs and spices in a piece of muslin, using either parsley, rosemary or thyme, or a combination of two or three of these herbs. Tie up the muslin securely, making sure the string is quite long so that you will be able to see it easily to remove the bouquet garni from the cooked dish.

Brown Stock

Per recipe: 100 mg sodium   30 calories

1 kg/2 lb beef or veal bones, broken
150 g/5 oz carrots, sliced
2 medium onions, sliced
2 sticks celery, chopped
8 peppercorns
bay leaf
pinch of dried mixed herbs
blade of mace
3 cloves
2 litres/3½ pints water

Put the bones and prepared vegetables in a roasting tin and bake them in a moderately hot oven (190 C, 375 F, gas 5) for about 15–30 minutes or until well browned. Transfer the cooked bones, without the vegetables, to a large heavy-based saucepan and add the peppercorns, bay leaf, mixed herbs, mace and cloves. Pour in the water and bring to the boil, then reduce the heat, cover the pan and simmer the stock for about 2 hours.

Add the vegetables and continue to simmer for a further 1 hour. Strain the stock, then set it aside to cool. Skim off the fat and scum from the surface of the stock before use.

If you are planning on freezing the stock, simmer it without a lid on the pan and remember to add more water before using it. **Makes about 900 ml/1½ pints**

Chicken Stock

Per recipe: 120 mg sodium   30 calories

225 g/8 oz veal bones
1 chicken carcass
chicken giblets
6 peppercorns
bouquet garni (page 20)
900 ml/1½ pints water
1 medium carrot, sliced
1 medium onion, diced
1 small leek, sliced
1 stick celery, chopped

Chop the bones into small pieces or ask your butcher to do so for you. Put the veal and chicken bones in a large saucepan with the giblets, peppercorns, bouquet garni and water. Bring to the boil, then reduce the heat and cover the pan. Simmer gently for about 1 hour. Remove the scum from the surface of the stock from time to time.

At the end of the cooking time add a further 200 ml/7 fl oz *cold* water and skim the stock again. Stir in the prepared vegetables and continue simmering, covered, for a further 2 hours. Strain, cool and skim off any scum and fat again. **Makes about 750 ml/1¼ pints**

Note: If you want to freeze the stock, simmer it without a lid on the pan so that the water will evaporate to give a concentrated result, but remember to add more water when you use the stock in recipes.

Sherried Consomme

Per portion: 25 mg sodium 35 calories

900 ml / 1½ pints Brown Stock (page 21)
50 g / 2 oz mushroom stalks
100 g / 4 oz lean minced beef
1 teaspoon concentrated tomato purée
whites and crushed shells of 2 eggs
75 ml / 3 fl oz sherry

Pour the stock into a large saucepan and add the mushroom stalks and mince, then stir in the tomato purée. Lightly whisk the egg whites and crush the shells, then add both to the pan. Bring to the boil, whisking the stock continuously. Make sure the heat is low so that the mixture rises but does not boil over. Without stirring, simmer the liquid very gently for 35 minutes.

Strain the consommé through muslin or a very clean teatowel, then return it to the rinsed out saucepan and heat it up. Stir in the sherry and serve. **Serves 4**

VARIATIONS

1 Very, fine strips of blanched carrot and celery can be added to the prepared consommé.

(Per portion: 25 mg sodium 35 calories)

2 Add a medium beetroot, grated, with the minced beef. As there is no salt in this recipe, the soup may be rather sweet. Counteract this by using very dry sherry or by adding a drop or two of lemon juice.

(Per portion: 50 mg sodium 45 calories)

French Onion Soup

Per portion with ordinary bread: 320 mg sodium   200 calories
Per portion with salt-free bread: 20 mg sodium   200 calories

450 g/1 lb onions, sliced
15 g/½ oz unsalted butter
900 ml/1½ pints Sherried Consommé (page 23)
freshly ground black pepper
about 1 tablespoon French mustard
4 slices French bread

Cook the onions in the butter in a saucepan for about 20 minutes or until tender and browned. Do not cook the onions over a high heat or they will burn, and remember to stir them frequently during cooking. Pour in the consommé and season with plenty of pepper. Bring to the boil, reduce the heat and simmer, covered, for 15 minutes. Meanwhile spread the mustard on the slices of French bread. Pour the soup into four individual, ovenproof soup dishes and place one slice of bread, mustard side up, in each bowl.

Using a spoon, press the bread down into the soup to soak it, then let it float to the surface. Place under a hot grill until golden brown and serve immediately. **Serves 4**

Tomato, Orange and Carrot Soup

Per portion: 25 mg sodium   100 calories

15 g/½ oz unsalted butter
675 g/1½ lb ripe tomatoes, chopped
1 medium onion, diced
225 g/8 oz carrots, sliced
bouquet garni (page 20)
slice of lemon
900 ml/1½ pints Chicken Stock (page 22)
1 large orange
15 g/½ oz arrowroot or cornflour

Melt the butter in a heavy-based saucepan, then add the tomatoes, onion and carrots and fry for 1 minute, without allowing them to brown. Add the bouquet garni and lemon, and pour in the stock. Bring to the boil, reduce the heat and cover the pan, then simmer the soup for about 30 minutes. Meanwhile, peel all the rind from the orange (without any of the pith) and cut it into fine shreds. Blanch the orange rind in boiling water for 1 minute. Drain and set aside. Remove the bouquet garni and press the soup through a sieve or blend it in a liquidiser.

Mix the arrowroot or cornflour with a little cold water until smooth. Reheat the soup, then, stirring continuously, pour the arrowroot or cornflour into the hot soup. Bring to the boil stirring continuously. Drain and set aside. Squeeze the juice from the orange and stir it into the soup. Remove the pan from the heat and add the drained orange zest. Serve immediately.
Serves 4

Tomato and Mushroom Soup

(Illustrated on page 33)

Per portion: 15 mg sodium   45 calories

1 large leek, sliced and thoroughly washed
1 large onion, chopped
1 clove garlic, crushed
1 teaspoon wine vinegar
8 ripe tomatoes, chopped
1 tablespoon concentrated tomato purée
4 large open mushrooms or 225 g/8 oz button mushrooms, diced
900 ml/1½ pints Chicken Stock (page 22)
bouquet garni (page 20)

Garnish
4 button mushrooms, sliced
chopped parsley

Place all the ingredients in a heavy-based saucepan and bring to the boil. Reduce the heat and simmer gently for 40 minutes. Cool slightly, then remove the bouquet garni and blend the soup in a liquidiser. Press through a fine sieve and reheat the soup before serving, garnished, if you like, with a few slices of button mushroom and parsley. **Serves 4**

Mushroom and Watercress Soup

Per portion: 10 mg sodium   95 calories

150 g/5 oz mushrooms
25 g/1 oz unsalted butter
150 g/5 oz onions, chopped
25 g/1 oz plain flour
1 litre/1¾ pints Brown Stock, heated (page 21)
2 teaspoons concentrated tomato purée
bunch of watercress
freshly ground black pepper
cayenne pepper

Remove the mushroom stalks and chop them, then chop half the mushroom caps. Melt the butter in a saucepan, add the onions with the chopped mushrooms and stalks, and cook for about 5 minutes. Stir in the flour, then gradually pour in the stock, stirring continuously and bring to the boil. Stir in the tomato purée, reduce the heat and cover the pan. Simmer gently for 10 minutes.

While the soup is cooking, slice the remaining mushroom caps finely. Discard any coarse stalks from the watercress and chop the leaves. Sieve or blend the soup in a liquidiser, then return it to the rinsed-out saucepan. Add the sliced mushrooms and watercress and season to taste with black pepper and cayenne. Simmer the soup for a further 2 minutes before serving. **Serves 4**

Cream of Artichoke Soup

Per portion with skimmed milk: 45 mg sodium   120 calories
Per portion with whole milk: 45 mg sodium   145 calories

450 g/1 lb Jerusalem artichokes
a little lemon juice
225 g/8 oz potatoes
1 small onion, diced
15 g/$\frac{1}{2}$ oz unsalted butter
600 ml/1 pint Brown Stock (page 21)
300 ml/$\frac{1}{2}$ pint milk or skimmed milk
$\frac{1}{2}$ teaspoon freshly grated nutmeg
freshly ground black pepper

Peel the artichokes and place them in a bowl of cold water with a little lemon juice added to prevent them from discolouring. Slice the prepared artichokes and potatoes, then fry them with the onion in the butter for 3 minutes. Do not allow the vegetables to brown. Pour in the stock and bring to the boil. Cover the saucepan and simmer the soup gently for about 25 minutes.

At the end of the cooking time, allow the soup to cool slightly, then press it through a sieve or blend it in a liquidiser. Stir in the milk and nutmeg and reheat but do not boil. Season to taste with freshly ground black pepper before serving. **Serves 4**

Spiced Potato and Onion Soup

(Illustrated on page 33)

Per portion: 20 mg sodium   100 calories

1 large onion
350 g / 12 oz potato
3 sticks celery
1 large parsnip
900 ml / 1½ pints Chicken Stock (page 22)
2 tablespoons concentrated tomato purée
generous pinch of oregano
pinch of ground cumin
1 teaspoon French mustard
freshly ground black pepper

Garnish
paprika
a few sprigs of fresh mint

Chop the onion, then cut the other vegetables into small chunks. Place all the vegetables in a heavy-based saucepan, then add the stock, tomato purée, oregano, cumin and French mustard. Bring to the boil, stirring, then cover and simmer gently for about 30 minutes, or until all the vegetables are tender.

Add black pepper to taste and serve, garnished with paprika and mint leaves. Alternatively, the soup can be pressed through a sieve or blended in a liquidiser for a smooth consistency. **Serves 4**

Chilled Yogurt and Cucumber Soup

Per portion with skimmed milk: 100 mg   75 calories
Per portion with whole milk: 100 mg sodium   85 calories

450 ml/¾ pint natural yogurt
½ large cucumber, peeled
1 clove garlic, crushed
1 lemon
150 ml/¼ pint milk or skimmed milk

Garnish
paprika
chopped parsley

Stir or lightly whisk the yogurt until it is smooth. Halve the cucumber lengthways and discard the seeds. Grate the flesh and stir it into the yogurt, then add the garlic.

Cut four thin slices from the lemon and keep these for garnishing the soup. Grate the rind from the remainder of the lemon and squeeze out the juice. Stir this rind and juice into the soup, then stir in enough milk to give the right consistency. Chill thoroughly before serving, garnished with the reserved lemon slices, paprika and chopped parsley. **Serves 4**

Starters

Many foods traditionally eaten as the first course are suitable for a low-sodium diet. Grapefruit, oranges, fruit and vegetable juices (but be careful about the canned varieties, and the Worcestershire sauce which is often added), avocado pears, eggs and salad vegetables are all low in sodium.

Bought pâtés, on the other hand, are rather salty and often quite fatty; instead of these, try the recipe for Chicken Liver Pâté on page 38: its's delicious and it doesn't contain any added salt. Served with some crisp fresh vegetables, like celery or carrot sticks, and home-made bread (recipes on pages 124 to 126), this pâté makes an excellent starter.

In winter, a hot first course to a meal is much better than a cold salad. You could simply served grilled grapefruit halves or a light soup, but if you are feeling more adventurous try some of the hot dishes in this section – they range from Baked Green Peppers to Scallop Eggs.

Baked Green Peppers

Per portion: 5 mg sodium   190 calories

2 small green peppers
75 g/3 oz brown rice
200 ml/7 fl oz Chicken Stock (page 22)
1 small onion, chopped
1 teaspoon corn oil
4 button mushrooms, chopped
50 g/2 oz shelled peas (fresh or frozen), cooked
2 tomatoes, peeled
50 g/2 oz pistachio nuts
150 ml/$\frac{1}{4}$ pint tomato juice

Cut each pepper in half lengthways. Scoop out and discard all the seeds and pith, leaving the stalks in place. Cook the pepper halves in boiling water for 3 minutes; drain thoroughly on absorbent kitchen paper.

Cook the rice in the stock, in a covered saucepan, for about 30 minutes, or until the grains are just tender. At the end of the cooking time all the stock should have been absorbed. Meanwhile, fry the onion in the oil until soft but not browned. Stir in the mushrooms and peas and remove the pan from the heat. Halve the tomatoes, remove all their seeds and chop the flesh, then mix them with the rice. Chop the nuts and add them to the rice mixture along with the onions and mushrooms. Divide this mixture between the peppers and arrange the halves in an ovenproof dish. Pour the tomato juice around the peppers and cover with cooking foil. Bake in a moderately hot oven (190 C, 375 F, gas 5) for 15 minutes. Serve immediately.
Serves 4

Note: To peel tomatoes, place them in a bowl and pour in enough boiling water to cover them completely. Leave the tomatoes for about $\frac{1}{2}$ to 1 minute, then drain them and remove the peel.

From the top: Tomato and Mushroom Soup (page 26) and Spiced Potato Soup (page 29)

Stuffed Tomatoes

Per portion: 40 mg sodium 80 calories

4 large beefsteak tomatoes

Stuffing

½ small onion, finely chopped
1 small clove garlic, crushed
1 teaspoon corn oil
100 g/4 oz minced veal
pinch of dried tarragon
freshly ground black pepper
2 teaspoons plain flour
1 teaspoon concentrated tomato purée
75 ml/3 fl oz Chicken Stock (page 22)

Cut off and reserve a small slice from the top of each tomato (opposite the stalk end). Using a small teaspoon, scoop out and discard the seeds from inside the tomatoes.

Mix the onion and garlic and fry them gently in the oil until soft but not browned. Add the veal and stir it to break up the pieces, then cook until lightly browned. Reduce the heat, then add the tarragon, pepper, flour and tomato purée. Still stirring, pour in the stock and bring to the boil; reduce the heat and simmer gently for 4 minutes. Use this meat mixture to fill the tomatoes. Replace the lids, then stand the tomatoes in a greased ovenproof dish. Cover and bake in a moderately hot oven (190 C, 375 F, gas 5) for about 15 minutes. Serve immediately, garnished with watercress. **Serves 4**

Note: This filling can also be used to stuff small green or red peppers.

Chicken Liver Pâtés (page 38) and Melon with Tomato
and Cucumber (page 41)

Mushroom Savouries

Per portion: 50 mg sodium   90 calories

4 large open mushrooms
1 small onion, chopped
1 clove garlic, crushed
1 teaspoon corn oil
40 g/1½ oz unsalted butter
2 eggs
2 tablespoons water
pinch of dried mixed herbs
freshly ground black pepper
1 tablespoon chopped parsley

Remove the stalks from the mushrooms and wipe the caps. Cook the onion and garlic in the corn oil until the onion is soft and set aside. Gently cook the mushroom caps in 15 g/½ oz of the butter for about 5 minutes.

Meanwhile, beat the eggs with the water, herbs and pepper to taste. Melt the remaining butter in a saucepan (preferably a non-stick one), then pour in the egg mixture and cook gently, stirring continuously, until the eggs set.

Spoon a little of the onion mixture on to each mushroom and top with the scrambled egg. Sprinkle with parsley and serve immediately. **Serves 4**

Scallop Eggs

Per portion with skimmed milk: 120 mg sodium   280 calories
Per portion with whole milk: 120 mg sodium   305 calories

1 large leek
4 eggs, hard boiled
450 g / 1 lb potatoes
1 small onion
15 g / $\frac{1}{2}$ oz unsalted butter
1 tablespoon chopped parsley

Sauce
15 g / $\frac{1}{2}$ oz unsalted butter
25 g / 1 oz plain flour
300 ml / $\frac{1}{2}$ pint milk or skimmed milk
freshly ground black pepper
generous pinch of tarragon

Discard most of the green part from the leek and slice the white very thinly. Wash thoroughly and cook in boiling water for 10 minutes. Drain the leeks and arrange them in four individual ovenproof dishes or shells. Cut the eggs in half lengthways and place one egg in each dish or shell.

Slice the potatoes, then cook them in boiling water until just tender and drain. Meanwhile, grate the onion and cook it in the butter for about 5 minutes. Mash the cooked potatoes, then add the onion and parsley and beat until smooth. Set aside to cool slightly.

To make the sauce, melt the butter in a saucepan. Stir in the flour and cook for a minute, then pour in the milk and bring to the boil, stirring continuously. Season to taste with pepper and add the tarragon. Pipe the potato around the edge of the dishes or shells, then pour the sauce over the eggs in the middle. Place under a medium-hot grill until golden and serve immediately.

Serves 4

Chicken Liver Pâté

(Illustrated on page 34)

Per portion: 80 mg 190 calories

350 g / 12 oz chicken livers
1 medium onion, chopped
1 clove garlic, crushed
25 g / 1 oz unsalted butter
2 teaspoons single or whipping cream
2 tablespoons brandy
freshly ground black pepper

Garnish
a few sprigs of parsley or thyme
bay leaves
juniper berries
2 slices orange or lemon

Roughly chop the chicken livers. Cook the onion and garlic in the butter until soft but not browned. Add the livers and continue to cook for about 10 to 15 minutes. Set aside to cool.

Blend the cooled mixture until smooth with the cream, brandy and black pepper to taste. Press into four individual dishes or ramekin dishes and smooth over the top. Pour a little melted butter over each dish of pâté and chill thoroughly.

Serve the pâté garnished with parsley or thyme, or bay leaves, juniper berries and quartered orange or lemon slices.
Serves 4

Grapefruit with Avocado

Per portion: 2 mg sodium 125 calories

2 large grapefruit
1 large ripe avocado pear
1 tablespoon olive oil
2 tablespoons lemon juice
freshly ground black pepper
pinch of dry mustard
a few mint leaves

Halve the grapefruit and cut between the membranes to loosen the flesh. Put the segments in a bowl and, using scissors, remove all the membranes from the skins. Halve the avocado, remove the stone and peel, and dice the flesh. Mix the avocado flesh with the grapefruit segments. Mix the oil, lemon juice, pepper and mustard in a screw-top jar and shake thoroughly. Chop all but four of the mint leaves and add the chopped mint to the dressing. Pour this dressing over the grapefruit, then spoon the mixture back into the fruit shells. Decorate with the reserved mint leaves and serve. **Serves 4**

Celeriac and Carrot Belle Hélène

Per portion: 55 mg sodium   70 calories

1 large celeriac root
2 large carrots
25 g/1 oz walnuts
25 g/1 oz raisins

Dressing
2 tablespoons wine vinegar
2 tablespoons olive oil
generous pinch of dry mustard
freshly ground black pepper
cayenne pepper

Peel and coarsely grate the celeriac and carrots. Chop the walnuts. Mix the celeriac, carrot, nuts and raisins in a salad bowl.

Pour all the dressing ingredients into a small screw-top jar and shake together until thoroughly mixed. Pour the dressing over the salad and toss to thoroughly coat all the ingredients.
Serves 4

Melon with Tomato and Cucumber

(Illustrated on page 34)

Per portion: 60 mg sodium   115 calories

1 ripe honeydew or cantaloupe melon
1 large cucumber
8 firm ripe tomatoes
2 tablespoons olive oil
1 tablespoon lemon juice
1 tablespoon white wine
generous pinch each of paprika, sugar and dry mustard
freshly ground black pepper
2 tablespoons chopped parsley
1 tablespoon chopped mint

Remove all the seeds from the melon, scoop out the flesh and cut it into dice. Peel and dice the cucumber. Peel the tomatoes (see note, page 32), then cut them into quarters and discard the seeds. Pour the olive oil into a screw-top jar with the lemon juice, wine, paprika, sugar, mustard and black pepper, then shake thoroughly. Place the melon, cucumber and tomato in a bowl, mix well and pour in the dressing. Toss the ingredients to coat them thoroughly, then serve chilled, sprinkled with parsley and mint. **Serves 4**

Pear and Walnut Salad

Per portion: 25 mg   220 calories

2 large ripe pears *or* 4 canned pear halves, drained
a little lemon juice
8 crisp lettuce leaves
75 g/3 oz walnuts
1 egg
2 tablespoons caster sugar
3 tablespoons tarragon vinegar
4 tablespoons whipping cream

Peel the pears, halve them and remove their cores. Brush the fruit with a little lemon juice to prevent it from discolouring. Arrange the lettuce leaves on four individual plates and put the pear halves, cut side down, on top. Chop the walnuts.

Crack the egg into a small bowl, then add the sugar and vinegar and stand the bowl over a pan of simmering water. Whisk the egg mixture until thick and pale. Remove from the heat and continue whisking until the mixture cools. Whip the cream until it begins to thicken, then fold it into the egg mixture. Spoon this dressing over pears. Top with the walnuts and serve. **Serves 4**

Fish Dishes

Despite its natural environment, white fish is low in sodium. Uncooked shell fish naturally has a higher sodium content and this is increased if it is bought ready cooked simply because shell fish is invariably cooked in salted water.

Smoked fish, like cured meats, contain a lot of sodium, so kippers, smoked haddock and smoked mackerel are to be used with care. Similarly, canned sardines, tuna, salmon and pilchards are very salty foods and should be replaced by the fresh alternatives whenever possible.

Nearly all bought prepared fish dishes, including fish in batter and breadcrumbs, contain added salt so these should be avoided. You can easily prepare batters and coatings for fish using salt-free ingredients.

Cod Fish Cakes

Per portion: 120 mg sodium   340 calories

450 g/1 lb potatoes
1 teaspoon lemon juice
2 tablespoons chopped parsley
generous pinch of chopped fresh basil
450 g/1 lb cod fillet
150 ml/¼ pint water
generous pinch of dried mixed herbs
1 slice of onion
freshly ground black pepper
25 g/1 oz unsalted butter, melted
50 g/2 oz fine oatmeal
25 g/1 oz sesame seeds
1 egg, beaten
corn oil for cooking

Garnish
1 lemon, cut into wedges
few sprigs of parsley

Cook the potatoes in boiling water, then drain and mash them with the lemon juice, parsley and basil. While the potatoes are cooking lay the fish fillet in a frying pan and pour in the water. Add the herbs and slice of onion, then simmer gently for about 15 minutes, or until the fish is cooked. Drain, remove the skin from the fish and flake the flesh removing any bones. Season the fish with black pepper and add the melted butter.

Mix the fish and potato together. Shape the mixture into eight equal-sized fish cakes. If they are fairly soft, chill the fish cakes until the mixture is firm. Mix the oatmeal and sesame seeds on a large plate. Coat the cakes first in beaten egg, then completely in the oatmeal mixture. Fry the cakes in a little corn oil or grill them very gently to heat the mixture through and brown the outside.

Drain the cooked fish cakes on absorbent kitchen paper and serve immediately, garnished with lemon wedges and parsley.
Serves 4

Cod Steaks with Spicy Creamed Potato

Per portion with low sodium chutney: 80 mg sodium 200 calories
Per portion with ordinary chutney: 85 mg sodium 205 calories

450 g/1 lb potatoes
freshly ground black pepper
1 tablespoon chopped parsley
generous pinch of nutmeg
15 g/$\frac{1}{2}$oz unsalted butter
1–2 teaspoons garam masala (page 99)
1 teaspoon lemon juice
4 cod steaks
300 ml/$\frac{1}{2}$ pint Court Bouillon (page 20)
1 tablespoon apricot chutney

Boil the potatoes until tender, then mash them with the pepper, parsley, nutmeg and butter. Mix the garam masala with the lemon juice and beat the paste into the mashed potato. Pipe the spiced potato round the edge of an ovenproof serving dish.

Poach the cod steaks in the court bouillon for about 15 minutes, then drain them and transfer them to the ovenproof serving dish, arranging the fish within the piped potato. Spread the apricot chutney over the fish and place the dish under a medium–hot grill to brown the potato. Serve immediately.
Serves 4

Haddock with Cinnamon Sauce

Per portion: 290 mg sodium   260 calories

675 g/1½ lb haddock fillet
300 ml/½ pint Court Bouillon (page 20)
bay leaf
about 100 ml/4 fl oz milk or skimmed milk
25 g/1 oz unsalted butter
25 g/1 oz plain flour
freshly ground black pepper
generous pinch of cinnamon
75 g/3 oz cooked crabmeat

Garnish
paprika
1 lemon, cut into wedges

Lay the haddock fillet in a frying pan or saucepan and pour in the court bouillon. Add the bay leaf, cover the pan and simmer gently for 15 minutes, or until the fish is cooked. Remove the fish from the pan and strain the cooking liquor into a measuring jug. Make this liquid up to 300 ml/½ pint with the milk or skimmed milk. Flake the fish off its skin and transfer it to an ovenproof serving dish removing all the bones.

Melt the butter in a small saucepan, stir in the flour, then gradually pour in the liquid. Bring to the boil, stirring continuously. Add black pepper and cinnamon, stir well and add the crabmeat. Pour this sauce over the flaked haddock and place it under a hot grill until golden and bubbling. Serve hot, garnished with a little paprika and lemon wedges. **Serves 4**

Stuffed Plaice Rolls

Per portion: 220 mg sodium   250 calories

50 g/2 oz long-grain rice
200 ml/7 fl oz Chicken Stock (page 22)
generous pinch of saffron strands
25 g/1 oz raisins
4 pistachio nuts, chopped
1 small onion, chopped
2 teaspoons oil
3 button mushrooms, sliced
$\frac{1}{2}$ beaten egg
8 plaice fillets
freshly ground black pepper
sprigs of watercress to garnish

Place the rice in a saucepan and pour in 150 ml/$\frac{1}{4}$ pint of the stock. Pound the saffron in a pestle and mortar, or with the back of a wooden spoon, then stir in just a little water. Add the saffron liquid to the rice, bring to the boil, then simmer, covered, for about 15 to 20 minutes or until the rice is tender and all the liquid has been absorbed. Add the raisins and nuts and set aside.

Cook the onion in the oil until soft but not browned, then add the mushrooms and cook for a further 2 minutes. Add this mixture to the rice and stir in the egg.

Lay the fish fillets skin side up and sprinkle with pepper. Divide the rice filling between the fillets, then roll them up from the tail end. Arrange the fish in a greased ovenproof dish, pour in the remaining stock and cover with cooking foil. Bake in a moderately hot oven (190 C, 375 F, gas 5) for 30 minutes. Serve hot, garnished with watercress. **Serves 4**

Sole Véronique

Per portion: 150 mg sodium   230 calories

6–8 sole fillets
6 tablespoons water
2 tablespoons white wine
2 slices of onion
freshly ground black pepper
100 g/4 oz green grapes
25 g/1 oz unsalted butter
15 g/½ oz plain flour
2 tablespoons whipping cream

Arrange the sole fillets in a greased ovenproof dish and pour in the water and wine. Add the onion, separated into rings, and season with pepper. Cover with cooking foil and bake in a moderate oven (180 C, 350 F, gas 4) for 15 to 20 minutes.

While the fish is cooking, halve the grapes and remove all their pips. Transfer the cooked fish to a serving dish and keep hot. Strain the cooking liquor. Melt the butter in a small saucepan and stir in the flour, then gradually add the fish liquor. Bring to the boil, stirring, then taste and add more pepper. Stir in the cream and remove the pan from the heat. Pour this sauce over the fish and scatter the grapes on top. Serve immediately. **Serves 4**

Skate with Pineapple and Kiwi Fruit

(Illustrated on page 51)

Per portion: 120 mg sodium   200 calories

4 wings of skate
freshly ground black pepper
25 g/1 oz unsalted butter · a little lemon juice
2 kiwi fruit, peeled and sliced
4 slices fresh pineapple, cored

Season the skate with pepper and fry it gently in the butter until lightly browned on both sides. Keep hot in a serving dish.

Add the lemon juice to the juices remaining in the pan. Stir well then add the prepared kiwi fruit and pineapple slices. Heat through and serve the fruit on the wings of skate. **Serves 4**

Baked Red Mullet

Per portion: 120 mg sodium   280 calories

4 red mullet, cleaned · 2 eggs, hard boiled
15 g/½ oz unsalted butter
1 medium onion, sliced
8 button mushrooms, sliced
cayenne pepper · freshly ground black pepper

Lightly rinse the body cavities of the fish. Chop the eggs finely. Melt the butter in a small saucepan, add the sliced onion and cook until soft but not browned. Stir in the mushrooms and cook for 1 to 2 minutes. Add the cayenne and freshly ground black pepper, then, off the heat, stir in the egg.

Divide the stuffing between the fish and press it well into the body cavities. Wrap each fish in greased greaseproof paper and lay them on a baking tray. Bake in a moderate oven (180 C, 350 F, gas 4) for about 25 to 30 minutes, or until the fish is cooked through. Transfer the paper-wrapped fish to warmed plates and serve immediately. **Serves 4**

Spinach-stuffed Trout

Per portion: 160 mg sodium   200 calories

4 trout, cleaned
175 g/6 oz cooked spinach, thoroughly drained
½ teaspoon freshly grated nutmeg
pinch of oregano
generous pinch of paprika
15 g/½ oz unsalted butter
1 small onion, chopped
50 g/2 oz button mushrooms, sliced

Garnish
1 lemon, sliced
sprigs of parsley

Lightly rinse the body cavities of the trout and remove their heads if you wish. Mix the spinach with the nutmeg, oregano and paprika. Melt the butter in a small pan, add the onion and cook until soft but not browned. Stir in the mushrooms and cook for 1 minute, then stir the mixture into the spinach.

Divide this spinach stuffing between the trout, pressing it well into the body cavities. Lay the fish in a greased ovenproof dish, then cover with cooking foil and bake in a moderate oven (180 C, 350 F, gas 4) for about 40 to 45 minutes or until the fish is cooked. Serve immediately, garnished with slices of lemon and sprigs of parsley. **Serves 4**

Spinach-stuffed Trout (above) and Skate with Pineapple and Kiwi Fruit (previous page)

Poultry

Chicken and turkey have become more popular in recent years, and have, to some extent, replaced roast beef or lamb for Sunday lunch as well as the cheaper cuts of meat served for mid-week meals. Not only is poultry economical compared with other meats, but chicken and turkey are also low in calories. This is true only if the skin is removed from the bird, preferably before you cook the meat. Chicken and turkey are traditionally served with bread-based stuffings, but bought bread has a high sodium content. To overcome this problem you can make your own salt-free bread and use it to prepare sage and onion stuffing in the usual way (without adding salt, of course) or you could try some of the stuffings which don't need bread at all. This chapter includes a few interesting recipes using apricots, nuts and rice.

It goes without saying that convenience food chicken products are out if you want to keep your sodium intake down. You can make your own version of deep-fried chicken by using breadcrumbs made from salt-free bread and, perhaps, mixing them with sesame seeds for extra flavour.

From the top: Turkey Stir-fry with Cranberries (page 60) and Chicken with Orange and Almonds (page 55)

Chicken and Carrot Casserole

Per portion: 120 mg sodium   160 calories

2 large carrots, sliced
1 medium onion, sliced
4 chicken joints, skinned
$\frac{1}{2}$ teaspoon oregano
300 ml/$\frac{1}{2}$ pint Chicken Stock (page 22)
1 tablespoon plain flour
freshly ground black pepper
orange slices to garnish

Place the carrots and onion in an ovenproof casserole. Lay the chicken joints on top and sprinkle with oregano. Pour in the stock, cover the casserole and cook in a moderate oven (180 C, 350 F, gas 4) for about 1$\frac{1}{2}$ hours or until the chicken is tender.

Transfer the chicken joints to a hot serving dish and arrange the carrots around them. Cover with cooking foil and keep the chicken hot. Mix the flour to a smooth paste with a little cold water. Pour the cooking liquor from the chicken into a saucepan and stir in the blended flour. Stirring continuously, bring the sauce to the boil. Season to taste with pepper. Strain the sauce if you like and serve it in a sauce boat to accompany the chicken. Garnish the chicken with orange slices before serving. **Serves 4**

Chicken with Orange and Almonds

(Illustrated on page 52)

Per portion: 75 mg sodium   230 calories

3 oranges
25 g/1 oz flaked almonds
4 chicken joints, skinned
1 tablespoon corn oil
freshly ground black pepper
2 pieces preserved stem ginger, chopped
sprigs of watercress

Peel the rind thinly from one of the oranges, then shred it and blanch it in boiling water for 2 minutes, or until tender; drain. Squeeze the juice from two oranges. Brown the almonds under a hot grill, turn them frequently and take care not to burn them.

Brush the chicken joints with oil, then brown them all over in a large frying pan which has a lid. Season with black pepper, then pour in the orange juice and cover the pan. Cook gently, turning the chicken occasionally, for about 45 minutes or until the chicken is cooked through.

Transfer the cooked chicken to a serving dish and keep hot. Squeeze the juice from the remaining orange and pour it into the pan. Add the blanched orange rind and ginger. Bring to the boil, then pour the sauce over the chicken and top with the toasted flaked almonds. Garnish with watercress and serve immediately. **Serves 4**

Chicken in Red Wine

Per portion: 75 mg sodium   350 calories

175 ml/6 fl oz red wine
2 tablespoons olive oil
freshly ground black pepper
bouquet garni (page 20)
4 chicken joints, skinned
1 small onion, chopped
100 ml/4 fl oz Chicken Stock (page 22)
100 g/4 oz button mushrooms, sliced
15 g/$\frac{1}{2}$ oz unsalted butter
1 tablespoon plain flour
sprigs of watercress to garnish

Mix the wine, oil, pepper and boquet garni. Place the chicken joints in a large dish and pour the wine marinade over them. Cover and set aside for at least 3 hours.

At the end of marinating time, remove the chicken from the marinade and place the joints in an ovenproof casserole with the onion, chicken stock and marinade. Cover and cook in a moderate oven (180 C, 375 F, gas 4) for about 1$\frac{1}{4}$ hours or until the chicken is cooked through and tender. Transfer the cooked chicken to a hot serving dish and keep hot.

Sauté the mushrooms in the butter for 1 minute add the flour and pour in the strained cooking juices from the chicken. Bring to the boil, then spoon the mushrooms in their sauce over the chicken. Serve any excess sauce separately to accompany the chicken. Garnish with watercress and serve immediately.
Serves 4

Chicken Breasts in Cream Sauce

Per portion: 120 mg sodium   300 calories

4 chicken breasts
1 small onion, very finely chopped
15 g/½ oz unsalted butter
5 button mushrooms, chopped
pinch of tarragon · freshly ground black pepper
50 g/2 oz minced veal
1 tablespoon single cream
1 egg white, lightly whisked

Sauce
15 g/½ oz unsalted butter
25 g/1 oz plain flour
175 ml/6 fl oz Chicken Stock (page 22)
3 tablespoons single cream
2 tablespoons white wine · 1 egg yolk
chopped parsley to garnish

Lay the chicken breasts between two sheets of greaseproof paper and beat them out until they are flat and thin. Fry the onion in the butter until soft. Add the mushrooms and cook for a further 3 minutes. Season with tarragon and pepper. Remove this mixture from the pan, then add the veal and cook for 10 minutes, or until the meat is broken up and browned.

Stir the cooked meat into the onion mixture. Mix in the cream and bind the mixture with the lightly whisked egg white. Divide the veal mixture between the chicken breasts, shaping it into a neat mound in the middle of each, and fold the chicken over to enclose the filling completely. Wrap each piece of chicken in greased cooking foil and bake in a moderately hot oven (190 C, 375 F, gas 5) for 1 hour.

Meanwhile make the sauce: melt the butter in a saucepan, add the flour and cook stirring for 1 minute. Pour in the stock, stirring continuously, and bring to the boil. Lower the heat and stir in the cream, wine and egg yolk. Heat through very briefly; do not allow the sauce to boil or it will curdle.

Arrange the chicken on a serving platter, pour over the sauce and serve, garnished with parsley. **Serves 4**

Chicken and Fruit Kebabs

Per portion: 70 mg sodium   160 calories

350 g/12 oz boneless cooked chicken
3 pineapple rings
½ red pepper
1 ripe fresh peach
1 teaspoon ground ginger

Cut the chicken into 2.5–cm/1–in cubes. Cut each pineapple ring into four chunks. Remove all the seeds and pith from the pepper and cut the flesh into squares. Blanch these pieces of pepper in boiling water for 1 minute, then drain them on absorbent kitchen paper. Peel and stone the peach and cut the flesh into cubes. Roll these pieces of fruit in ginger.

Thread all the prepared ingredients on to four metal skewers, arranging the chicken, fruit and pepper alternately. Cook the kebabs under a hot grill until lightly browned. Serve immediately. **Serves 4**

Turkey Braise

Per portion: 230 mg sodium   350 calories

2 teaspoons corn oil
1 stick celery, chopped
2 carrots, sliced
1 onion, sliced
1-kg/2-lb turkey roast
300 ml/½ pint Chicken Stock (page 22)
bouquet garni (page 20)
1 tablespoon plain flour
freshly ground black pepper
cayenne pepper

Heat the oil in a flameproof casserole, add the vegetables and fry for 5 to 10 minutes, or until the vegetables are lightly browned. Rest the turkey roast on top of the vegetables and pour in the stock. Add the bouquet garni and bring to the boil. Reduce the heat, cover and simmer gently for about 2 hours. Alternatively cook the braise in a moderately hot oven (190 C, 375 F, gas 5) for the same length of time.

Remove the joint from the casserole and transfer it to a hot serving dish; keep hot. Blend the flour with a little cold water to make a smooth paste. Stir this into the liquid in the casserole and bring to the boil, stirring continuously to prevent lumps from forming. Season to taste with pepper and a little cayenne.

To serve, remove the vegetables from the sauce (use a draining spoon) and arrange them around the joint. Pour a little of the sauce over both the meat and the vegetables, then serve the remainder separately. **Serves 4**

Note: Prepared, boneless joints of turkey are available either chilled or frozen in a variety of different sizes. They are often encased in a string wrapping which must be kept on the joint until the roast is cooked, then removed before carving.

Turkey Stir-fry with Cranberries

(Illustrated on page 52)

Per portion: 95 mg sodium   200 calories

450 g / 1 lb uncooked boneless turkey breast
4 sticks celery
4 carrots
1 bunch spring onions
25 g / 1 oz unsalted butter
100 g / 4 oz cranberries
1 tablespoon demerara sugar
juice of 1 orange

Cut the turkey into strips. Cut the celery, carrots and spring onions into fine strips and set aside.

Melt the butter in a frying pan, then add the turkey and cook, stirring continuously, until the pieces are well browned and cooked through. Remove the turkey from the pan and keep it hot. Add the celery and carrots to the fat remaining in the pan and cook until they are tender but still crisp. Stir in the spring onions, cranberries, sugar and orange juice, then replace the turkey in the pan. Cook for about 15 minutes, or until the cranberries are soft but not mushy. Serve the turkey, arranged in a dish with the vegetables. **Serves 4**

Stuffings for Chicken and Turkey

Bought stuffing mixes usually contain salt. Stuffing prepared at home from bought bread will also contain salt; however, there are alternatives. You can always make up a traditional stuffing mixture using home-made salt-free bread but there is a wide variety of other recipes which are quick and easy to prepare. Here are just three ideas; each recipe is enough for stuffing an average-sized chicken. Make sure that a frozen chicken or turkey is thoroughly defrosted before you stuff and cook it. The stuffing mixture can be pressed under the skin covering the breast of the bird instead of filling the body cavity. Often, some of the stuffing can be pressed under the skin and the remainder used to fill the body cavity.

Rice and Apricot Stuffing

Per recipe: 160 mg sodium   930 calories

100 g/4 oz dried apricots, chopped
225 g/8 oz cooking apples, peeled and cored
25 g/1 oz unsalted butter
25 g/1 oz flaked almonds
100 g/4 oz cooked long-grain rice
freshly ground black pepper
grated rind and juice of $\frac{1}{2}$ lemon
1 egg, beaten

Use dried apricots which are fairly soft and not bone hard. Mix all the ingredients together and use only just enough beaten egg to bind the stuffing.

Veal and Mushroom Stuffing

Per recipe: 320 mg sodium   725 calories

40 g/1½ oz unsalted butter
2 medium onions, chopped
225 g/8 oz lean minced veal
5 button mushrooms, chopped
2 teaspoons chopped parsley
freshly ground black pepper
generous pinch each of cayenne pepper and mace
1 egg, beaten

Melt the butter in a frying pan, add the onions and veal and cook, stirring frequently, for 10 minutes. Remove the pan from the heat, then add all the remaining ingredients, using only just enough beaten egg to bind the stuffing.

Pork, Celery and Walnut Stuffing

Per recipe: 200 mg sodium   700 calories

25 g/1 oz unsalted butter
2 sticks celery, chopped
1 onion, chopped
4 tablespoons chopped walnuts
175 g/6 oz lean minced pork
50 g/2 oz chesnut purée

Melt the butter in a frying pan, add the celery and onion and cook until the onion is just soft. Stir in the walnuts and continue to cook for 2 minutes. Remove the mixture from the pan. Add the minced pork and cook, breaking the meat up as it cooks, until lightly browned. Remove the pan from the heat, stir in the chestnut purée and the cooked onion mixture. Use as required.

Meat

Meat naturally contains more sodium than fruit and vegetables but fresh meat is still low in sodium content compared with most of the canned and cured meats and convenience meat dishes which are now available.

Practically every recipe you read for a meat dish tells you to sprinkle the joint, chops or pieces of meat with salt and pepper before cooking. Those meat dishes which rely on fruits for some of their flavour also tell you to add salt; but it really is quite unnecessary. Simply leaving salt out of some recipes works well, but for others the resulting saltless taste is bland and thin. By using herbs and a selection of other ingredients, like mushrooms and tomatoes, the lack of salt doesn't matter. However, take care when buying tomato purée to make sure that it has no salt added. Worcestershire sauce is an excellent seasoning when used in tiny amounts, but it does contain salt so use it very carefully.

Cured meats like ham and bacon contain sodium not only in the salt but also in the curing ingredients. You can see just how much sodium is added in the table on pages 15 to 18. A little bacon added to a recipe may not seem to matter, but remember to count the sodium that it contains into your daily total.

Paprika Beef

Per portion: 130 mg sodium   290 calories

700 g / 1½ lb stewing beef
1 tablespoon corn oil
1 large onion, sliced
2 carrots, sliced
1 large green pepper
300 ml / ½ pint Brown Stock (page 21)
bouquet garni
1 tablespoon paprika
25 g / 1 oz plain flour
freshly ground black pepper

Cut the beef into 3.5-cm / 1½-in cubes, discarding any visible fat. Heat the oil in a large heavy-based saucepan, then add the meat and fry quickly, turning the pieces frequently until brown. Reduce the heat, then add the onion and carrot and continue to cook for 5 minutes.

Meanwhile, halve the pepper, discard the seeds and pith and cut the flesh into thin strips. Add the pepper strips to the meat with the stock, bouquet garni and paprika. Bring to the boil, then reduce the heat, cover and simmer very gently for 1½ hours or until the meat is tender. Mix the flour to a smooth paste with a little cold water. Over a very low heat, gradually pour this into the casserole, stirring vigorously to prevent lumps from forming. Bring to the boil, cook for a minute and season to taste with pepper before serving. **Serves 4**

Port and Beef Casserole

Per portion: 130 mg sodium   420 calories

1 kg/2 lb stewing beef
1 tablespoon corn oil
1 tablespoon plain flour
450 ml/¾ pint Brown Stock (page 21)
150 ml/¼ pint port
2 cloves garlic, crushed
cayenne pepper
4 large open mushrooms
25 g/1 oz unsalted butter
2 tablespoons chopped parsley

Cut the beef into large cubes, discarding any fat and gristle. Brown the meat quickly in the oil, then sprinkle in the flour and stir in the stock. Bring to the boil and stir in the port, garlic and cayenne. Transfer to an ovenproof casserole, cover and cook in a moderately hot oven (190 C, 375 F, gas 5) for 1½ hours or until the meat is tender.

Meanwhile, slice the mushrooms thickly and fry them in the butter for 1 minute. Stir the mushrooms into the meat, sprinkle with chopped parsley and serve immediately. **Serves 4**

Chilli con Carne

(Illustrated on page 85)

Per portion: 95 mg sodium   310 calories

175 g/6 oz red kidney beans
450 g/1 lb lean minced beef
2 medium onions, chopped
1 tablespoon corn oil
2 teaspoons chilli powder
2 teaspoons paprika
1 teaspoon French mustard
1 clove garlic, crushed
2 teaspoons tomato purée
450 ml/$\frac{3}{4}$ pint Brown Stock (page 21)

Soak the beans overnight in enough water to cover. Next day drain the beans, place them in a saucepan with enough fresh water to cover. Bring to the boil and boil hard for about 5 minutes, then simmer for about 1$\frac{1}{2}$ hours or until the beans are tender. Drain and set aside.

Cook the beef and onions in the oil until lightly browned. Stir in the chilli powder, paprika, mustard, garlic, tomato purée and stock, cover and simmer very gently for 1 to 1$\frac{1}{2}$ hours or until the meat is tender. Add the red kidney beans and cook for a further 5 minutes. **Serves 4**

Roast Veal with Lemon Stuffing

Per portion with ordinary bread: 200 mg sodium   450 calories
Per portion with salt-free bread: 170 mg sodium   450 calories

75 g/3 oz wholemeal breadcrumbs
freshly ground black pepper
50 g/2 oz blanched almonds, chopped
grated rind and juice of 1 lemon
generous pinch each of rosemary and thyme
1 small onion, chopped
45 g/1½ oz unsalted butter
1 egg, beaten
150 ml/¼ pint white wine
1.75-kg/4-lb shoulder of veal, boned
arrowroot to thicken

Mix the breadcrumbs with pepper to taste and the almonds. Stir in the lemon rind and juice and the herbs. Fry the onion in 15 g/½ oz of the butter until it is soft but not browned, cool, then add it to the stuffing. Mix in only just enough of the egg to bind the stuffing without making it wet.

Press the stuffing into the meat and secure the joint neatly in shape with string or metal skewers. Stand the joint in a roasting tin which is just large enough to take the joint, dot the meat with the remaining butter and pour in the wine. Cover with cooking foil and roast the veal in a moderately hot oven (190 C, 375 F, gas 5) for 1½ hours. Remove the foil, baste the joint and increase the temperature to hot (220 C, 425 F, gas 7). Continue cooking for a further 20 to 30 minutes.

Transfer the cooked joint to a heated serving dish, then thicken the pan juices, if you like, with a little arrowroot blended with cold water. Alternatively, simply strain the juices into a sauce boat to serve with the joint. **Serves 6**

Tarragon Veal

Per portion with skimmed milk: 140 mg sodium   210 calories
Per portion with whole milk: 140 mg sodium   230 calories

450 g/1 lb veal fillet
freshly ground black pepper
1 tablespoon corn oil
1 small onion, finely chopped
25 g/1 oz plain flour
300 ml/½ pint milk or skimmed milk
150 ml/¼ pint Chicken Stock (page 22)
generous pinch of tarragon
juice of ½ lemon
1 tablespoon chopped parsley

Cut the veal fillet into four equal-sized steaks. Sprinkle each steak with pepper and fry the meat quickly in the oil to brown both sides, then remove it from the pan.

Add the onion to oil remaining in the frying pan and cook until soft but not brown. Stir in the flour, then pour in the milk and stock. Bring to the boil, reduce the heat and stir in the tarragon. Replace the veal, cover the pan and simmer gently for about 20 minutes, or until the meat is tender.

Transfer the veal to a heated serving dish and keep hot. Add the lemon juice to the sauce, then pour this over the veal. Garnish with chopped parsley and serve. **Serves 4**

Veal à la Crème

Per portion: 100 mg sodium   200 calories

4 veal escalopes, beaten out thinly
freshly ground black pepper
25 g/1 oz unsalted butter · 1 tablespoon lemon juice
6 button mushrooms, sliced · 3 tablespoons brandy
2 tablespoons whipping cream

Season the escalopes with pepper. Using half the butter, melted in a frying pan, cook the escalopes until well browned on both sides and cooked. Remove from the pan and keep hot.

Add the lemon juice, mushrooms, brandy and cream, stir in the rest of the butter and heat through. Pour the sauce over the meat and serve immediately. **Serves 4**

Tipsy Liver

Per portion: 110 mg sodium   290 calories

450 g/1 lb calves' liver
plain flour seasoned with pepper and cayenne pepper
25 g/1 oz unsalted butter
1 tablespoon corn oil · 1 small onion, chopped
150 ml/¼ pint Brown Stock (page 21)
3 tablespoons sweet sherry · chopped parsley to garnish

Cut the liver into thin strips and toss them in the seasoned flour. Shake off any excess flour. Melt the butter with the oil in a frying pan and cook the onion for about 5 minutes or until soft but not browned. Remove from the pan, then add the liver and cook it quickly to brown the pieces. Remove the liver from the pan and set it aside with the onion.

Pour the stock and sherry into the pan, stir and boil hard to reduce by about one third. Replace the liver and onion and simmer very gently for 5 minutes. Serve immediately, garnished with chopped parsley. **Serves 4**

Lamb Meatballs with Tomato Sauce

Per portion: 110 mg sodium 230 calories

350 g/12 oz lean minced lamb
3 dried apricots, chopped
4 walnut halves, chopped
1 teaspoon concentrated tomato purée
15 g/½ oz plain flour
cayenne pepper
1 teaspoon chopped thyme
freshly ground black pepper
1 egg, beaten
1 quantity Tomato Sauce (page 98)

Mix the lamb, apricots, walnuts and tomato purée. Mix in the flour, cayenne, thyme and pepper, then add just enough egg to bind the ingredients together. Shape the meat into 24 small meatballs, arrange them in a roasting tin and bake in a moderate oven (180 C, 350 F, gas 4) for 20 to 30 minutes.

Meanwhile prepare the tomato sauce according to the recipe instructions. Serve the meatballs with the sauce poured over. **Serves 4**

Lamb with Redcurrant Gravy

(Illustrated on page 85)

Per portion: 85 mg sodium 260 calories

2 best end of neck lamb joints
a few sprigs of fresh rosemary
freshly ground black pepper
1 tablespoon redcurrant jelly
1 teaspoon arrowroot
3 tablespoons red wine
sprigs of watercress to garnish

Chine the two best end joints – there should be six or seven cutlets in each one. Scrape the ends of the bones clean and arrange the two joints so that the bones interlock alternately in a guard of honour. Tie the bones together with string at intervals. Place the joint in a greased baking tray that is just large enough to hold the joint. Sprinkle the meat with rosemary and black pepper and cover with cooking foil. Roast in a moderate oven (180 C, 350 F, gas 4) for about 2 hours. Remove the foil, increase the oven temperature to hot (220 C, 425 F, gas 7) and continue to cook for a further 20 to 30 minutes or until the meat is crisp and brown. Transfer the joint to a heated serving plate and remove the string. Keep hot.

Strain off all but 1 tablespoon of the fat and scrape all the meat juices off the pan. Add the redcurrant jelly and wine and bring to the boil. Blend the arrowroot with a little cold water, then pour a little of the hot sauce on it. Return the arrowroot to the pan and bring back to the boil, stirring. Garnish the joint with watercress and serve, handing the sauce separately to accompany the lamb. **Serves 6**

Note: Lamb chops can be grilled or fried and served with the sauce from the above recipe as illustrated on page 85.

Pork Chops in Cider

Per portion: 90 mg sodium   275 calories

4 pork chops with kidney
350 g/ 12 oz cabbage
15 g/½ oz unsalted butter
1 medium onion, chopped
1 small dessert apple
150 ml/¼ pint dry cider
75 ml/3 fl oz Brown Stock (page 21)
freshly ground black pepper
1–2 teaspoons arrowroot
1 small dessert apple, sliced and cored to garnish

Trim all the fat from the pork chops. Shred the cabbage finely. Melt the butter in a flameproof casserole, add the onion and cook for 3 minutes. Add the cabbage, stir and cook gently for a further 2 minutes.

Meanwhile peel, core and slice the apple, then lay the pieces on top of the cabbage. Arrange the chops in the casserole then pour in the cider and stock. Season to taste with pepper, cover the casserole and cook in a moderately hot oven (190 C, 375 F, gas 5) for about 1½ hours, or until the meat is tender.

Blend the arrowroot with a little cold water until smooth. Remove the chops from the casserole and keep them hot. Carefully strain a little of the cooking liquor on to the arrowroot, then return to the casserole, carefully stirring it into the liquid. Bring to the boil, then replace the chops and serve immediately, garnished with the apple slices. **Serves 4**

Pork with Raisin Sauce

Per portion (without pork fat): 55 mg sodium 200 calories

1 kg/2 lb loin of pork joint
3 tablespoons orange juice
40 g/1½ oz soft brown sugar
200 ml/7 fl oz dry cider
50 g/2 oz raisins
8 cloves
5-cm/2-in piece cinnamon stick
1 teaspoon arrowroot

Score the rind and fat of the pork and set the joint in a roasting tin just large enough to hold it. Pour the orange juice over the pork, cover with cooking foil and roast in a moderately hot oven (190 C, 375 F, gas 5) for about 1½ hours. Increase the temperature to hot (220 C, 425 F, gas 7), remove the foil and continue to cook for a further 30 minutes or until the rind is crisp and brown.

Meanwhile, mix the sugar, cider, raisins, cloves and cinnamon in a small saucepan. Simmer, covered, for 15 minutes. Remove the cloves and cinnamon. Blend the arrowroot with a little cold water until smooth. Stirring, pour a little of the hot sauce on to the arrowroot, return the liquid to the pan and bring back to the boil.

Serve the roast pork carved into slices, with the sauce handed separately. **Serves 6**

Pork Fillet with Apricots

(Illustrated on page 85)

Per portion: 120 mg sodium 350 calories

575 g/1¼ lb pork fillet
1 (227-g/8-oz) can apricot halves, drained (reserve the liquid)
about 150 ml/¼ pint Brown Stock (page 21)
15 g/½ oz unsalted butter
1 tablespoon corn oil
1 small onion, chopped
1 tablespoon plain flour
1 tablespoon cider vinegar

Discard any fat from the pork and cut the meat into cubes. Make the apricot juice up to 300 ml/½ pint with brown stock.

Melt the butter in a flameproof casserole, add the oil and heat through. Brown the pork in the fat, reduce the heat and add the onion. Cook gently, stirring, for 2 minutes. Sprinkle in the flour, then gradually stir in the liquid. Bring to the boil, stir in the vinegar and cover the casserole. Simmer gently for about 30 minutes or until the meat is tender. Add the apricot halves and heat through.

Serve the casserole, if you like, with Nutty Rice (page 91).
Serves 4

Vegetables

The thought of not adding salt to vegetable cooking water is, for many people, too dreadful to contemplate. Yet those who have become used to not ladling in the salt are totally happy with plain boiled vegetables.

It does take time to get used to unsalted peas and cabbage, but as long as you cut down gradually it is quite possible. In the transition period, make sure you use plenty of pepper and other flavouring ingredients. Unsalted potatoes are probably the most difficult vegetables to accept, but baking or roasting them helps a great deal.

Green vegetables, like cabbage, can be made more interesting by adding caraway seeds or sliced apples and onion; carrots can be glazed with orange juice, and glazed onions are delicious.

Potato Puffs

(Illustrated on page 86)

Whole recipe: 100 mg sodium   1200 calories

These are a bit fiddly to make, but worth the effort.

25 g/1 oz unsalted butter
1 large egg yolk
350 g/12 oz potatoes, boiled and mashed

Choux Pastry
4 tablespoons water
20 g/¾ oz unsalted butter
3 tablespoons plain flour
1 egg, beaten
oil for deep frying

Beat the 25 g/1 oz butter and egg yolk into the potatoes. In a small saucepan, heat the water and butter gently until the fat melts, then bring quickly to the boil. As soon as the water boils tip in all the flour. Remove the pan from the heat. Stir vigorously so that the mixture forms a paste which leaves the sides of the pan clean. Allow the paste to cool for about 3 minutes, then gradually beat in the egg. Beat thoroughly until the paste is smooth and glossy.

Gradually beat the potato into the choux pastry. Put the mixture into a large piping bag fitted with a plain 1-cm/½-in nozzle and pipe 5-cm/2-in lengths of mixture on to a greased baking tray. Heat the oil to 190 C/375 F then gradually slide the strips of mixture into the hot oil and fry them until they are puffed and golden brown – about 4 minutes. Drain on absorbent kitchen paper and keep hot while the rest of the mixture is being cooked, but for no longer than 10 to 15 minutes. **Makes about 36**

Caramelled Potatoes

Per portion: 15 mg sodium   270 calories

1 kg/2 lb potatoes
25 g/1 oz caster sugar
25 g/1 oz unsalted butter
1 tablespoon hot water

Cut the potatoes into 1-cm/½-in dice, then cook them in boiling water for 4 minutes and drain well.

Put the sugar in a small, heavy-based saucepan with 1 teaspoon cold water. Heat gently to dissolve the sugar, then bring to the boil. Allow to boil, without stirring, until a golden caramel is formed. Immediately remove the pan from the heat and, very carefully because the mixture may spit, add the butter and 1 tablespoon hot water. Stir the caramel and return the pan to the heat. If the pan is too small to hold the potatoes, then transfer the caramel to a larger saucepan first.

Add the potatoes to the caramel and cook gently, stirring or shaking the pan occasionally, for about 5 minutes, or until the potatoes are cooked and golden. **Serves 4**

Stuffed Baked Potatoes

Here are a few suggestions for fillings which are low in sodium but taste excellent with a plain baked potato. Select large (about 200 g/7 oz each in weight), good quality potatoes for baking. Scrub the skin well and remove any blemished areas. Bake the potatoes in a moderately hot oven (200 C, 400 F, gas 6) for about 1 to 1¼ hours. Slice a small piece from the top of each potato and scoop out most of the flesh. Mash the scooped-out potato and mix it with any of the following ingredients. Pile the filling back into the potato shells, then return them to the oven for about 5 to 10 minutes to heat through.

Per portion: 15 mg sodium   175 calories

Light Fillings

1 Mix 50 g/2 oz canned mixed sweet corn and red peppers and 1 tablespoon home-made chutney (page 92) into the potato.

Per portion: 20 mg sodium   260 calories

2 Add 25 g/1 oz chopped walnuts and 25–50 g/1–2 oz cottage cheese with chives.

Per portion: 130–240 mg sodium   340–370 calories

3 Add 50 g/2 oz flaked, cooked white fish, 2 teaspoons chopped fresh chives and freshly ground black pepper to taste.

Per portion: 55 mg sodium   220 calories

4 Thoroughly mash or chop 75 g/3 oz cooked vegetables, for example carrots, parsnips, French beans or sweet corn, season with ground black pepper and mix into the potato.

Per portion: 20 mg sodium   200 calories

More Substantial Fillings

Instead of mixing in the filling as above, the potato can be mashed with a little skimmed milk, then piped to form a border around each potato shell, leaving the middle hollow. Fill the middle with any of the following.

1 Crack an egg into each potato, then return them to the oven for about 5 minutes, or until the eggs are cooked to taste.

Per portion: 90 mg sodium   265 calories

2 Chop 1 lamb's kidney and cook it with 1 small chopped onion, ground black pepper, a little Chicken Stock (page 22) and 1 tablespoon dry sherry for about 5 minutes. While this mixture is cooking heat the piped potato in the oven. Spoon the kidney mixture into the potato and serve.

Per portion: 60 mg sodium 280 calories

3 Fry 50 g/2 oz lean minced beef until browned, then add a little curry paste, about 2 tablespoons Brown Stock (page 21), 1 teaspoon concentrated tomato purée and 1 teaspoon apricot jam. Fill the potato with this mixture and bake for 5 minutes.

Per portion: 80 mg sodium 272 calories

Vegetable Bake

Per portion: 170 mg sodium 130 calories

225 g/8 oz potatoes
225 g/8 oz parsnips
225 g/8 oz swede
25 g/1 oz unsalted butter
1–2 tablespoons milk or skimmed milk
freshly ground black pepper
generous pinch of nutmeg
100 g/4 oz cottage cheese

Cook all the vegetables separately in boiling water until they are tender, then drain well. Mash the potato and parsnip together, adding half the butter and the milk, and season with pepper and nutmeg. Mash the swede, adding plenty of freshly ground black pepper and the remaining butter.

Place half the potato in the base of a greased ovenproof dish (one about 20 cm/8 in. in diameter). Lightly smooth the top then spread the mashed swede over. Top with the remaining potato. Spread the cottage cheese over the vegetables and bake in a moderately hot oven (200 C, 400 F, gas 6) for about 15 to 20 minutes or until the cheese is lightly browned. Serve immediately. **Serves 4**

Orange Glazed Carrots

Per portion: 50 mg sodium   100 calories

450 g/1 lb carrots
1 tablespoon water
15 g/½ oz caster sugar
25 g/1 oz unsalted butter
2 tablespoons orange juice

Peel and slice the carrots then cook them in the minimum amount of water until just tender. Drain well and set aside.

In a small saucepan, heat the water and sugar until the sugar has dissolved. Boil, without stirring, until a pale golden caramel is formed. Carefully add the butter, then the orange juice. Tip in the carrots and toss over a low heat to heat them through and coat the pieces with the caramel. If the saucepan containing the caramel is too small to hold all the carrots, then place the vegetables in another pan and pour the caramel over them. **Serves 4**

Pepperoni

Per portion: 10 mg sodium   25 calories

2 large red peppers
2 large green peppers
1 large onion, sliced
1 clove garlic, crushed
pinch of basil
1 tablespoon corn oil
freshly ground black pepper

Halve the peppers and discard all the seeds and pith from inside. Discard the stalks and cut the flesh into thin strips.

Put the peppers and onion, garlic and basil in a large frying pan with the oil and cook gently for about 15 minutes. The vegetables should still be crisp. Grind black pepper over the top and serve immediately. **Serves 4**

Carrots and Broccoli with Parsley Sauce

Per portion: 30 mg sodium   70 calories

225 g/8 oz brocolli
225 g/8 oz baby carrots, quartered
15 g/½ oz unsalted butter
15 g/½ oz plain flour
150 ml/¼ pint Chicken Stock (page 22)
2 tablespoons chopped parsley
generous pinch of oregano
freshly ground black pepper

Trim any tough stalks from the broccoli. Cook the carrots and broccoli spears, separately, in boiling water, until just tender. If possible, broccoli is better simmered in a large frying pan so that the heads are not overcooked. Drain the vegetables and place them in a heated serving dish, then keep hot.

Melt the butter and stir in the flour. Stirring, add the stock and bring to the boil. Add the parsley, oregano and black pepper, cook for a minute before pouring the sauce over the cooked vegetables. Serve immediately. **Serves 4**

Glazed Onions with Peas

Per portion: 5 mg sodium 80 calories

25 g/1 oz caster sugar
1 tablespoon water
100 g/4 oz small pickling onions
2 tablespoons Brown Stock (page 21)
350 g/12 oz shelled peas
1 teaspoon chopped mint

Place the sugar and water in a saucepan, bring to the boil and boil without stirring until light golden in colour. Add the onions and toss to coat them. Transfer to a greased roasting tin and pour in the stock. Cook, uncovered, in a moderately hot oven (190 C, 357 F, gas 5) for about 1 hour. Very small onions will take a shorter time to cook. Add more water during cooking if necessary – no liquid should be left at the end of the cooking time.

Lightly cook the peas, drain them and add the mint. Transfer to a heated serving dish, then stir in the onions and serve immediately. **Serves 4**

Caraway Cabbage

Per portion: 15 mg sodium   100 calories

25 g/1 oz unsalted butter
1 small onion, sliced
1 cooking apple, peeled, cored and sliced
350 g/12 oz cabbage, shredded
freshly ground black pepper
1 tablespoon caraway seeds
2 tablespoons water

Melt the butter in a flameproof casserole and fry the onion for 5 minutes without allowing the slices to brown. Lay the slices of apple on top, then add a layer of cabbage. Season with pepper and sprinkle the caraway seeds over. Add the water, cover and simmer gently for about 40 minutes. Alternatively, cook the cabbage in a moderately hot oven (190 C, 375 F, gas 5) for 45 minutes. Add a little more water during cooking if necessary. Mix the cabbage with the onion and apple before serving. **Serves 4**

Ratatouille

(Illustrated on page 86)

Per portion: 15 mg sodium   35 calories

3 medium courgettes
1 small aubergine · 3 large ripe tomatoes
1 medium onion, sliced
1 clove garlic, crushed
generous pinch of oregano · pinch of basil
a little Chicken Stock (page 22)

Slice the courgettes and aubergines. Cut the aubergines in quarters before slicing them if they are very large. Peel the tomatoes (see page 32) and quarter them; discard the seeds.

Put the courgettes, onion, aubergines and garlic in a covered frying pan with the herbs and stock. Simmer very gently for about 25 minutes or until the onion and aubergines are cooked. Add the tomato and heat through before serving. **Serves 4**

Leek Purée

Per portion: 65 mg sodium   40 calories

2 large leeks, sliced and washed
350 g / 12 oz turnips, sliced
200 ml / 7 fl oz Chicken Stock (page 22)
1 large onion, chopped
1 tablespoon chopped parsley
generous pinch of tarragon
generous pinch of ground coriander
freshly ground black pepper
cayenne pepper

Put the leeks, turnips, stock and onion in a large saucepan. Add the herbs and coriander and simmer for about 40 minutes or until the leeks are soft. You may need to add a little extra stock during the cooking time, but all the liquid should have evaporated by the time the leeks are cooked.

Allow the leeks to cool slightly then purée them leaving a few small pieces of vegetable in the mixture. Turn the purée into a non-stick frying pan, season with the black pepper and cayenne and heat through gently, stirring occasionally. Serve immediately. **Serves 4**

From the top: Pork Fillet with Apricots (page 74) served with Nutty Rice (page 91); Lamb with Redcurrant Gravy (page 71) served with courgettes; Chilli con Carne (page 66) served with a baked potato with soured cream and chives

Stuffed Aubergines

Per portion: 40 mg sodium   300 calories

4 aubergines
grated rind and juice of 1 lemon
225 g/8 oz red lentils
1 large onion, chopped
2 cloves garlic, crushed
3 tablespoons oil
freshly ground black pepper
2 tablespoons chopped fresh coriander leaves

Garnish

1 lemon, cut into wedges
sprigs of coriander

Halve the aubergines, then scoop out and dice all the flesh. Reserve the skins, sprinkling the inside with lemon juice to prevent them from discolouring.

Wash the lentils, then place them in a saucepan and cover with plenty of water. Bring to the boil, reduce the heat and simmer gently for 10 minutes, or until the lentils are tender but not mushy. Meanwhile, fry the onion and garlic in the oil until soft but not browned. Season with pepper and stir in the lemon rind. Add the aubergine flesh and cook until just soft.

Drain the lentils and add them to the stuffing with the chopped coriander. Cover the pan and leave over a very low heat to keep hot. Quickly blanch the aubergine skins in boiling water until they are just tender. Do not overcook the shells or they will collapse. Drain thoroughly.

Fill the aubergines with the lentils and serve immediately, garnished with lemon wedges and coriander sprigs. **Serves 4**

From the top: Potato Puffs (page 76), Stuffed Aubergines (above) and Ratatouille (page 83)

Savoury Fried Rice

Per portion: 25 mg sodium   170 calories

25 g / 1 oz unsalted butter
100 g / 4 oz long-grain rice
1 small onion, chopped
1 clove garlic, crushed
300 ml / ½ pint Chicken Stock (page 22)
freshly ground black pepper

Melt the butter in a saucepan, add the rice and fry until the grains are lightly browned. Add the onion and garlic and continue to cook until the onion is soft. Carefully pour in the stock and bring to the boil, then cover the pan and simmer for about 10 minutes. Season to taste with ground pepper. At the end of the cooking time the rice should have absorbed all the water. Fluff up the grains with a fork before serving the rice.
Serves 4

Tomato Filled Rice Ring

Per portion: 50 mg sodium   270 calories

200 g/7 oz long-grain rice
generous pinch of saffron strands
1 medium onion, chopped
25 g/1 oz unsalted butter
750 ml/1¼ pints Chicken Stock (page 22)
freshly ground black pepper

Filling

½ cucumber
4 large tomatoes
1 large onion, chopped
generous pinch of dried mixed herbs
freshly ground black pepper

Put the rice, saffron, onion and butter in a large saucepan and cook gently for 4 minutes. Pour in the stock, bring to the boil, cover and simmer very gently for about 10 to 15 minutes or until the rice is just tender. Add a little more water if necessary during cooking, but all the liquid should be absorbed at the end of the cooking time. Season to taste with pepper and press into an oiled 7-in/18-cm ring mould. Cover with cooking foil and place in a moderate oven (180 C, 350 F, gas 4) for 10 minutes.

Meanwhile, prepare the filling. Peel and dice the cucumber. Peel and quarter the tomatoes (see note, page 32) and remove all their seeds. Put all filling ingredients in a small pan and heat gently for 5 minutes.

Invert the hot rice on to a serving plate, carefully lift off the mould and fill with the tomato mixture. Serve immediately.
Serves 4

Brown Rice Paella

Per portion: 90 mg sodium   285 calories

100 g/4 oz long-grain rice
300 ml/½ pint Chicken Stock (page 22)
50 g/2 oz shelled peas
50 g/2 oz drained canned sweet corn
4 button mushrooms, sliced
25 g/1 oz pistachio nuts
25 g/1 oz sultanas
25 g/1 oz dried apricots, chopped
100 g/4 oz boneless cooked chicken, diced
150 g/5 oz cooked haddock

Cook the rice in the stock, in a covered saucepan, for about 30 minutes, or until the grains are tender. Check the rice after about 20 minutes to make sure that it does not overcook. All the stock should be absorbed by the end of the cooking time.

While the rice is cooking, cook and drain the peas, then mix them with the sweet corn. Blanch the mushrooms for 3 minutes in water, then drain them and mix into the rice together with the sweet corn mixture and all the remaining ingredients. Toss well to mix all the ingredients and serve immediately. **Serves 4**

Rice Ideas

Plain rice, cooked without any salt, does taste rather bland, but there are ways of cheering it up. The more interesting varieties of rice have more flavour than some of the easy-cook types; for example, try brown rice, basmati rice or some of the wild rice mixtures. Not only is the flavour of these types of rice better, but they also have an interesting texture. Instead of cooking the rice in just water try using chicken stock (page 22) alternatively, try some of the ideas given below.

HERB RICE   Add chopped fresh herbs to the hot cooked rice. Try a mixture of several different herbs or select those which will complement the main dish; for example try rosemary and parsley or mint with lamb, sage and thyme with pork and tarragon with fish or poultry.

Per 100-g/4-oz cooked portion: negligible sodium   135 calories

LEMON OR ORANGE RICE   Add freshly grated orange or lemon rind to the freshly cooked rice. Stir in some chopped fresh parsley. Lemon rice goes very well with fish dishes and orange-flavoured rice is excellent with pork.

Per 100-g/4-oz cooked portion: negligible sodium   135 calories

PEPPERED RICE   Fry some chopped green or red peppers, or a mixture of both, with chopped onion in oil or unsalted butter. Toss these into the cooked rice just before serving.

Per 100-g/4-oz cooked portion: negligible sodium   200 calories

SPICED RICE   Add a cinnamon stick, some cloves and cardamoms to the rice when you put it into the saucepan. Sprinkle a little freshly ground coriander over the cooked rice just before it is served. This goes particularly well with curried dishes.

Per 100-g/4-oz cooked portion: negligible sodium   135 calories

NUTTY RICE   Add chopped walnuts or flaked almonds to the cooked rice with some chopped fresh parsley and fried chopped green peppers and onions if you like. Season the rice with freshly grated nutmeg.

Per 100-g/4-oz cooked portion: negligible sodium   about 300 calories

RICE SALAD   Add chopped spring onions, lightly cooked vegetables and herbs to freshly cooked rice, then pour in some French Dressing (page 100) and leave the salad to cool before serving.

Per 100-g/4-oz cooked portion: negligible sodium   about 300 calories

Pineapple and Apricot Chutney

Per recipe: 300 mg sodium   1960 calories

450 g / 1 lb cooking apples
1 large onion, chopped
200 g / 7 oz light soft brown sugar
450 ml / $\frac{3}{4}$ pint wine vinegar
1 teaspoon ground cinnamon
generous pinch of nutmeg
1 ripe fresh pineapple
450 g / 1 lb fresh or canned apricots
450 g / 1 lb dried apricots

Peel, core and chop the apples. Mix them with the onion. Dissolve the sugar in the vinegar in a large saucepan. Add the apple and onion, cinnamon and nutmeg. Bring to the boil, cover the pan and simmer gently for 15 minutes.

Meanwhile cut the pineapple into small pieces and chop both the fresh and dried apricots (remember to remove all the peel, stones and inedible bits if fresh fruit is used). Add the fruit to the pan, cover and continue to simmer for 30 minutes. Cool slightly, then pot the chutney in sterilised jars with screw tops. Cool, cover, label and store. **Makes about 2 kg / 4$\frac{1}{2}$ lb**

Salad Dressings and Sauces

Many dishes, from meat and fish to raw vegetable salads, only become palatable when a flavourful sauce is added. Packet sauces may be convenient but they are also salty. It may seem impossible to make an acceptable white sauce without adding salt, but with some imaginative use of herbs and a little education of the taste buds it is quite possible.

Hollandaise sauce, French dressing and mayonnaise can all be made without salt and, of course, curry sauce is so flavoursome that salt is totally unnecessary. Try making your own real curry powder from the basic spice ingredients. The range of flavours you can achieve is enormous, and curry does not have to be mouth-burning hot.

Basic White Sauce

Per recipe with skimmed milk: 530 mg sodium   250 calories
Per recipe with whole milk: 530 mg sodium   340 calories

300 ml/$\frac{1}{2}$ pint milk or skimmed milk
1 small onion, sliced
2 cloves
1 small carrot, sliced
bouquet garni (page 20)
5 peppercorns
blade of mace
15 g/$\frac{1}{2}$ oz unsalted butter
15 g/$\frac{1}{2}$ oz plain flour

Put the milk, onion, cloves, carrot, bouquet garni, peppercorns and mace into a saucepan, bring to the boil, then simmer very gently for 15 minutes. Strain the milk.

Melt the butter in the rinsed-out saucepan, add the flour and cook gently, stirring, for 1 minute. Gradually pour in the flavoured milk and bring to the boil, stirring continuously.
Makes about 300 ml/$\frac{1}{2}$ pint

Note: This is a recipe for a basic sauce to which you can add whatever flavouring ingredients you wish. To make up for the fact that the sauce contains no salt, add freshly ground black pepper to taste, chopped fresh herbs or dry mustard. By adding a little single or double cream, or extra unsalted butter, you can enrich the sauce. This recipe can also be used as a base for mushroom sauce, onion sauce or parsley sauce.

Savoury Cream Sauce

Per recipe with cream: 35 mg sodium   420 calories
Per recipe with evaporated milk: 120 mg sodium   310 calories

1 small onion, chopped
1 tablespoon corn oil
15 g/½ oz plain flour
75 ml/3 fl oz Court Bouillon (page 20)
cayenne pepper
½ teaspoon ground ginger
2 tablespoons chopped parsley
generous pinch of tarragon
50 ml/2 fl oz whipping cream

Fry the onion in the oil for 3 minutes, until soft but not brown. Stir in the flour, then gradually pour in the court bouillon. Bring to the boil, stirring, reduce the heat and add all the remaining ingredients. Simmer gently for 5 minutes and strain before serving. **Makes about 200 ml/7 fl oz**

Hollandaise Sauce

Per recipe: 30 mg sodium   600 calories

4 tablespoons wine vinegar
6 peppercorns
blade of mace
1 slice of onion
2 egg yolks
50 g/2 oz unsalted butter
freshly ground black pepper

Put the vinegar, peppercorns, mace and onion in a small saucepan and boil hard until reduced in quantity to 2 tablespoons. Strain the liquid into a small basin.

Beat the egg yolks and add them to the reduced liquid, then stand the bowl over a pan of hot water. Whisking continuously, add small knobs of the butter until all the butter has melted into the sauce. Do not allow the water to boil or the sauce will curdle. When the butter has melted add black pepper to taste and continue to cook, whisking, until the sauce is thick. Do not overcook the sauce. Remove from the heat, stir occasionally and allow to cool slightly, then serve warm. **Makes about 150 ml/¼ pint**

Note: This is a rich sauce so you only need to use small amounts for each dish.

Mustard Sauce

Per recipe: negligible sodium content   375 calories

25 g/1 oz unsalted butter
15 g/½ oz plain flour
200 ml/7 fl oz water
freshly ground black pepper
1 teaspoon lemon juice
1 tablespoon French mustard

Melt the butter in a saucepan, stir in the flour and cook for a few seconds. Add the water, a little at a time, beating all the time, and bring to the boil. Add pepper to taste and the lemon juice, then stir in the mustard. **Makes 300 ml/½ pint**

Horseradish Sauce

Per recipe: 50 mg sodium   550 calories

150 ml/¼ pint whipping cream
freshly ground black pepper
1 teaspoon made mustard
1 teaspoon sugar
1 tablespoon wine vinegar
50 g/2 oz grated horseradish

Whip the cream until it is just beginning to thicken, then stir in the remaining ingredients. **Makes about 300 ml/½ pint**

97

Tomato Sauce

Per recipe (300 ml/$\frac{1}{2}$ pint):   60 mg sodium   100 calories

225 g/8 oz ripe tomatoes
1 carrot
1 small onion
15 g/$\frac{1}{2}$ oz unsalted butter
2 teaspoons plain flour
150 ml/$\frac{1}{4}$ pint Chicken Stock (page 22)
freshly ground black pepper
pinch of caster sugar
bouquet garni (page 20)
1 teaspoon concentrated tomato purée

Chop the tomatoes, carrot and onion. Fry these vegetables in the butter for 5 minutes without allowing them to brown. Stir in the flour, then gradually pour in the stock, stirring continuously, and bring to the boil.

Add the remaining ingredients, cover the pan and simmer for 30 minutes. Remove the bouquet garni and press the sauce through a fine sieve. Reheat and use as required. **Makes about 300 ml/$\frac{1}{2}$ pint**

Curry Sauce

Per recipe: 110 mg sodium   370 calories

1 medium onion, chopped
15 g/½ oz unsalted butter
1 teaspoon concentrated curry paste
2 teaspoons garam masala
generous pinch of ground ginger
2 teaspoons plain flour
300 ml/½ pint Chicken Stock (page 22)
small piece of coconut cream *or* 2 tablespoons grated fresh
coconut
1 tablespoon redcurrant jelly
2 teaspoons lemon juice
25 g/1 oz raisins

Put the onion, butter, curry paste, garam masala and ginger in a saucepan and cook gently for about 3 minutes. Stir in the flour, then gradually stir in the stock. Bring to the boil, reduce the heat, cover the pan and simmer for 20 minutes.

Meanwhile, if you are using coconut cream, infuse it in a few tablespoons of hot water. Add the fresh coconut or diluted coconut cream, redcurrant jelly, lemon juice and raisins to the sauce. Heat through, stirring occasionally, and use as required. **Makes about 450 ml/¾ pint**

Note: Garam masala can be bought, but it can also be made at home by mixing equal amounts of the following ground spices: cumin, mace, cardamom, nutmeg, cloves and cinnamon.

Mayonnaise

Per recipe: 15 mg sodium   1080 calories

1 egg yolk
pinch of tarragon
$\frac{1}{4}$ teaspoon dry mustard
cayenne pepper
100 ml/4 fl oz olive or corn oil
1–2 tablespoons wine vinegar
1 tablespoon chopped parsley
1 teaspoon chopped chives

Beat the egg yolk with the tarragon, mustard and pepper. Gradually beat in the oil, adding it drop by drop at first then, after adding about 2 tablespoons, in teaspoonfuls, beating in each addition well. Stir in the vinegar, parsley and chives. Add a little cold water or more vinegar if the sauce is too thick.
Makes about 150 ml/$\frac{1}{4}$ pint

French Dressing

Per recipe: negligible sodium content   2700 calories

300 ml/$\frac{1}{2}$ pint olive oil
150 ml/$\frac{1}{4}$ pint wine vinegar
generous pinch of dry mustard
freshly ground black pepper

Place all the ingredients together in a small screw-top jar and shake vigorously until the dressing has emulsified.

VARIATIONS

1 For a herb dressing, add a generous pinch of chopped mixed fresh herbs and a little chopped mint.
2 Add just chopped fresh tarragon to taste.
3 For a less tangy dressing, use 75 ml/3 fl oz lemon juice in place of the vinegar.
4 For a slightly spicy dressing, use cider vinegar instead of the wine vinegar and add 2 cloves. Allow the dressing to stand for 1 to 2 hours and strain it before serving.

Supper Dishes, Savouries and Snacks

What do you eat with pre-dinner drinks if crisps and salted peanuts are taboo? Is there anything left? Not on the supermarket shelves, but there are plenty of snacks that you can make at home and many of them are far lower in calories than the fatty crisp-type nibbles. Crudités with a variety of dips are delicious, and a lot healthier for children as well as adults.

The most widely used ingredient in savouries and supper dishes must be cheese. Unfortunately, hard cheeses contain a great deal of salt. To some extent cottage cheese can be substituted, but there is a limit to that. The recipes in this chapter will help to fill the supper slot without adding lots of salt.

Onion Quiche

Per portion (cut into four): 140 mg sodium 630 calories
Per portion (cut into six): 90 mg sodium 420 calories

1 quantity Shortcrust Pastry (page 115)
675 g/1½ lb onions, chopped
50 g/2 oz unsalted butter
freshly ground black pepper
generous pinch of nutmeg
2 eggs
150 ml/¼ pint milk or skimmed milk
cayenne pepper
75 g/3 oz low-fat curd cheese

Make up the pastry according to the recipe instructions, then roll it out and use to line a 20-cm/8-in dish or tin.

Fry the onions in the butter until they are soft but not brown. Season with black pepper and nutmeg. Beat the eggs with the milk and cayenne. Cut the cheese into small pieces and add it to the egg mixture. Spread the onions in the base of the flan and pour in the egg mixture. Bake in a hot oven (220 C, 425 F, gas 7) for 5 minutes, then reduce the temperature to moderately hot (190 C, 375 F, gas 5) and cook for about 35 minutes or until the filling is set and golden brown. Serve hot or cold. **Serves 4 to 6**

VARIATION

Pepperoni Quiche: Instead of using the onions as above, substitute the recipe for Pepperoni on page 80. Continue as above.

Clockwise from the top: Oatcakes (page 116) and Gingernuts (page 123), Cheeseboard Ideas (page 113), Pepperoni Quiche (above), Celery and Cucumber Boats and Curry Tomatoes (both on page 112)

Mixed Omelette

Per portion: 200 mg sodium   290 calories

This is so called because you can use almost any left over cooked food in the filling! As an example I've chosen cooked vegetables and cold lamb.

2 eggs
1 tablespoon water
freshly ground black pepper
25 g/1 oz unsalted butter
50 g/2 oz cooked mixed vegetables
25 g/1 oz mushrooms, sliced
25 g/1 oz cooked lamb, finely chopped
1 teaspoon redcurrant jelly
1 tablespoon chopped parsley

Beat the eggs with the water and black pepper. In a small pan heat half the butter and add the vegetables, mushrooms, lamb and jelly. Leave over a low heat while you make the omelette.

Melt the remaining butter in a frying pan and pour in the egg mixture. Cook until the underneath is set then lift the sides to allow the uncooked mixture to run down on to the hot pan. Spoon the hot vegetable mixture on top of the set omelette, fold it in half and slide it out of the pan on to a hot plate. Sprinkle with chopped parsley and serve at once. **Serves 1**

From the top: Macaroons (page 122), Boiled Fruit Cake (page 117) and Fruit Bread (page 119)

Eggs en Cocotte

Per portion: 85 mg sodium   200 calories

15 g/½ oz unsalted butter
100 g/4 oz cooked sweet corn
1 tablespoon chopped parsley
4 large eggs
4 tablespoons whipping cream
cayenne pepper

Melt the butter and use it to grease four cocotte dishes or individual ovenproof dishes. Divide the sweet corn and parsley between the dishes. Drop an egg into each and top with a little cream. Stand the dishes in a roasting tin and pour in enough hot water to come halfway up the sides of the dishes. Bake in a moderate oven (180 C, 350 F, gas 4) for about 7 minutes. Sprinkle with cayenne and serve immediately. **Serves 4**

Onion Scramble

Per portion: 180 g sodium   300 calories

2 eggs
2 tablespoons skimmed milk
freshly ground black pepper
1 small onion, chopped
50 g/2 oz unsalted butter
1 tomato, peeled (see note, page 32) and chopped

Beat the eggs with the milk and pepper. Fry the onion in half the butter until soft but not browned, then stir in the tomato. Use the remaining butter to scramble the eggs in a non-stick saucepan and top with the onion mixture. Serve immediately. **Serves 1**

Toasted Sandwiches

Use the breads on page 124 to 126 or ordinary breads which contain salt. For each person allow 2 slices of bread. Toast one slice on one side only, and toast the other slice on both sides. Spread any of the following fillings on the untoasted side and grill to heat through. Top with the remaining slice of toast and serve immediately.

Fillings

1 Unsalted butter, sliced tomato, cottage cheese and chives with the chutney on page 92. (**With ordinary bread: 660 mg sodium 350 calories; With unsalted bread: 225 mg sodium 350 calories**)

2 Sliced cooked chicken, chutney (page 92) and cucumber slices. (**With ordinary bread: 460 mg sodium 270 calories; With unsalted bread: 30 mg sodium 270 calories**)

3 1 slice roast beef, 1 sliced tomato and horseradish sauce from page 97. (**With ordinary bread: 460 mg sodium 280 calories; With unsalted bread: 30 mg sodium 280 calories**)

4 1 sliced hard-boiled egg, sprigs of watercress and sliced tomato. (**With ordinary bread: 510 mg sodium 280 calories; With unsalted bread: 80 mg sodium 280 calories**)

5 A few chopped dates mixed with low-fat curd cheese, 1 tablespoon chopped walnuts. After toasting, add a few crisp lettuce leaves before topping with the second slice of toast. (**With ordinary bread: 560 mg sodium 350 calories; With unsalted bread: 125 mg sodium 300 calories**)

Crudités and Savoury Dips

Crudités

Cut sticks of celery, carrot and red and green peppers into thin strips. Place the vegetables in a bowl of cold water to crisp them up. After at least 30 minutes soaking, drain the crudités and arrange them on serving platters. Cut some radishes in half, and offer some shelled walnuts too.

Cheese and Pineapple Dip

Per recipe: 610 mg sodium   410 calories

50 g/2 oz canned crushed pineapple
225 g/8 oz low-fat curd cheese
1–2 tablespoons soured cream

Make sure the pineapple is well drained. Mix it with the cheese and just enough soured cream to give a firm dipping consistency. **Serves 4**

Onion and Mushroom Dip

Per recipe: 340 mg sodium   360 calories

1 small onion, finely chopped
1 clove garlic, crushed
3 button mushrooms, chopped
cayenne pepper
15 g/$\frac{1}{2}$ oz unsalted butter
100 g/4 oz low-fat curd cheese
1–3 tablespoons soured cream

Mix the onion with the garlic. Sprinkle the mushrooms with cayenne pepper. Melt the butter in a small pan and fry the onion and mushrooms for 10 minutes. Cool thoroughly, then mix with the cheese and enough soured cream to give the right consistency. **Serves 4**

Celery and Walnut Dip

Per recipe: 260 mg sodium   290 calories

2 sticks celery, very finely chopped
1 eating apple, peeled, cored and grated
2 tablespoons chopped walnuts
2 teaspoons lemon juice
2 tablespoons natural yogurt
50 g/2 oz cottage cheese

Mix all the ingredients and place the dip in a bowl. Chill lightly before serving. **Serves 4**

Avocado Dip

Per recipe: 120 mg sodium   300 calories

1 ripe avocado pear
1 clove garlic, crushed
2 teaspoons lemon juice
about 150 ml/$\frac{1}{4}$ pint natural yogurt
freshly ground black pepper

Halve the avocado, remove the stone and scoop out the flesh. Mash the avocado with the garlic and lemon juice, then add just enough yogurt to give the right consistency. Season with black pepper before serving. **Serves 4**

Savoury Eclairs

Choux Pastry

75 g / 3 oz plain flour
50 g / 2 oz unsalted butter
150 ml / ¼ pint water
2 eggs, lightly beaten

Sift the flour into a basin. Heat the butter and water together until the butter melts, then bring to the boil and tip in all the flour. Stir well until the mixture forms a ball of paste which leaves the sides of the pan clean. Remove from the heat and cool until just warm, then beat in the eggs, a little at a time. Beat thoroughly until the mixture is smooth and very glossy. Put the mixture in a piping bag fitted with a plain nozzle and pipe 5-cm / 2-in lengths on to a greased baking tray.

Bake at (200 C, 400 F, gas 6) for 25 to 35 minutes. Immediately they are removed from the oven, split the éclairs down the long side to allow the steam to escape. Fill the éclairs with any of the following mixtures.

Egg Mayonnaise

Per recipe: 480 mg sodium 1500 calories

2 hard-boiled eggs
1 tablespoon mayonnaise (page 100)
1 tablespoon natural yogurt
a few sprigs of watercress
cayenne pepper

Chop the eggs finely and mix them with the mayonnaise and yogurt. Discard any coarse stalks from the watercress, chop the leaves and add them, with the cayenne, to the egg mixture.

Haddock and Chives

Per recipe: 540 mg sodium   1440 calories

175 g/6 oz fresh haddock fillet
150 ml/¼ pint Court Bouillon (page 20)
1 tablespoon mayonnaise (page 100)
1 tablespoon natural yogurt
1 teaspoon chopped chives

Poach the fish in the court bouillon for 15 minutes. Drain and flake the cooked fish, discarding all skin and bone. Mix the fish with the mayonnaise and yogurt to coat, then stir in the chives.

Curried Chicken

Per recipe: 500 mg sodium   1620 calories

150 g/5 oz cooked chicken meat
1 tablespoon mayonnaise (page 100)
1–2 teaspoons curry powder
1 tablespoon raisins

Chop the chicken finely and mix it with the mayonnaise and curry powder. Stir in the raisins.

Celery and Cucumber Boats

(Illustrated on page 103)

Each piece: 10 mg sodium 7 calories

3 celery sticks
1 large cucumber
100 g/4 oz low-fat curd cheese
2 tablespoons crushed pineapple
paprika

Wash the celery and cut it into 5-cm/2-in lengths. Cut the cucumber into 1-cm/½-in lengths and scoop out most of the flesh but do not cut right through the skin. Drain the pineapple well and mix it with the curd cheese. Fill the celery and cucumber hollows with this mixture and sprinkle with paprika. **Makes about 40**

Curry Tomatoes

(Illustrated on page 103)

Each tomato: 30 mg sodium 15 calories

12 cherry tomatoes (very small sweet tomatoes)
100 g/4 oz low-fat curd cheese
1–2 teaspoons curry powder
2 teaspoons mayonnaise (page 100)

Cut the tops off the tomatoes (reserve these caps for later) and scoop out the seeds. Thoroughly mix the cheese and curry powder, then fold in the mayonnaise. Pipe this mixture into the tomato shells and replace the tops. **Makes 24**

Cheeseboard Ideas

(Illustrated on page 103)

Unfortunately many cheeses have a high sodium content. Cream cheese and curd cheese have the lowest sodium content (see chart on page 15), so for occasions when you want to prepare a cheeseboard as part of a meal, or even for a snack, you can present a selection of flavoured soft cheeses. Serve the cheese with Oatcakes (page 116) or Gingernuts (page 123). The following serve 4 to 6 persons.

Herb Cheese: Add 2 tablespoons chopped parsley, or a mixture of chopped fresh herbs, to 225 g/8 oz cream or curd cheese. Stir in the herbs and add 1 crushed clove of garlic. Season the cheese with a little black pepper, then turn it out on to a large piece of cling film. Pat the cheese down with the back of a wooden spoon to make it into a round shape. Fold the cling film around the cheese to cover it completely, then shape the mixture into a circle measuring about 2.5 cm/1 in deep. Chill until firm.

To serve, put the cheese round on a board and cover the outside with more chopped fresh herbs, carefully pressing them on with a palette knife.

(Per whole cream cheese: 680 mg sodium 990 calories)
(Per whole curd cheese: 680 mg sodium 320 calories)

Walnut Cheese: Follow the instructions for Herb Cheese, but substitute 50 g/2 oz chopped walnuts for the herbs and omit the garlic. Shape the cheese as above, chill it, then press chopped walnuts on to the outside before serving.

(Per whole cream cheese: 680 mg sodium 1250 calories)
(Per whole curd cheese: 680 mg sodium 580 calories)

Peppercorn Cheese: Again follow the recipe for Herb Cheese, but this time mix coarsely crushed black peppercorns into the cheese. Continue as above, chilling the cheese thoroughly, then press some coarsely ground black pepper on to the outside before serving.

(Per whole cream cheese: 680 mg sodium 990 calories)
(Per whole curd cheese: 680 mg sodium 320 calories)

Baking

In some cookery books there are still recipes that contain the obligatory pinch of salt in pastry to be used in sweet flans, or in cakes and biscuits with plenty of sugar. That really is unforgivable because the salt adds nothing to the flavour, so just leave the salt out of sweet recipes.

When it comes to bread we are up against a real problem. Of all the foods we eat, bread is probably the one which needs salt most for flavour, but you can get used to salt-free bread, particularly if you make some of the flavoured breads in this chapter. You can always continue to eat normal bread and count the sodium as part of the daily total. But do try some of the herb breads in this section first; with a little perseverance you may well be surprised to find that you really don't mind eating bread which has been made without salt.

Shortcrust Pastry

Per recipe: 5 mg sodium   2060 calories

175 g/6 oz plain flour
40 g/1½ oz unsalted butter
40 g/1½ oz white cooking fat
2 tablespoons cold water

Sift the flour into a bowl and rub in the fat until the mixture looks like fine breadcrumbs. With a fork, mix in just enough cold water to make a soft, but not sticky, dough. Knead together very lightly and chill well.

Rich Shortcrust Pastry

Per recipe for savoury: 20 mg sodium   1570 calories
Per recipe for almond (below):   20 mg sodium   1640 calories

175 g/6 oz plain flour
100 g/4 oz unsalted butter
25 g/1 oz caster sugar (for sweet dishes only)
1 egg yolk
a little milk or skimmed milk

Sift the flour into a bowl, then rub in the butter until the mixture looks like fine breadcrumbs. Stir in the sugar, if used. With a fork, mix in the egg yolk and just enough milk to bind the mixture. Knead lightly and chill before use.

Note: This is suitable for sweet flans and, without the sugar, for savoury dishes, such as quiches.

VARIATION

Use 25 g/1 oz ground almonds in place of 25 g/1 oz of the flour. Reduce the butter to 90 g/3½ oz.

Baking Powder

Per recipe: nil mg sodium   nil calories

This normally contains sodium bicarbonate. The amount depends on the brand but it is always quite large. However, an effective raising agent can be made up at home from potassium rather than sodium based ingredients. A pharmacist will supply them.

50 g/2 oz cornflour
15 g/½ oz potassium bicarbonate
100 g/4 oz potassium bitartrate

Mix all the ingredients together in a completely dry jar and screw down the lid so that the contents are airtight. Use 2 teaspoons for each 450 g/1 lb plain flour.

Oakcakes

(Illustrated on page 103)

Per recipe metric quantities: 35 mg sodium   635 calories
Per recipe imperial quantities: 40 mg sodium   710 calories

175 g/6 oz fine oatmeal
50 g/2 oz plain flour
¼ teaspoon potassium bicarbonate
25 g/1 oz white cooking fat
a little boiling water

Mix the oatmeal, flour and bicarbonate. Melt the fat and add it to the dry ingredients with just enough boiling water to make a soft dough. Mix well and roll out very thinly to form a circle. Transfer the dough to a greased baking tray and mark it into eight wedges.

Cook in a moderate oven (180 C, 350 F, gas 4) for about 1 to 1½ hours or until crisp. Cool on a wire rack.

Note: This mixture can also be cut into 2-cm/1-in rounds before baking, then used as the base for savouries and canapés.

Boiled Fruit Cake

(Illustrated on page 104)

Per recipe: 330 mg sodium   4120 calories

350 g/12 oz mixed dried fruit
25 g/1 oz glacé cherries, quartered
175 g/6 oz unsalted butter
175 g/6 oz demerara sugar
50 g/2 oz soft brown sugar
2 eggs, beaten
225 g/8 oz plain flour
1 teaspoon Baking Powder (opposite)
1 teaspoon mixed spice

Put the dried fruit and cherries in a saucepan, add just enough water to cover the fruit, then simmer for 5 minutes. Drain.

Cut the butter into small pieces and add them to the fruit. Stir in the sugars and eggs. Sift the flour, baking powder and spice together twice. Fold into the fruit. Grease and line a 20-cm/8-in round cake tin, turn the mixture into it and bake the cake at (160 C, 325 F, gas 3) for 1½ hours.

To test if the cake is cooked insert a metal skewer into it. If the skewer comes out clean of mixture the cake is cooked. Turn out and cool the cake on a wire rack.

Dark Gingerbread

Per recipe metric quantities: 225 mg sodium   2000 calories
Per recipe imperial quantities: 240 mg sodium   2300 calories

100 g/4 oz unsalted butter
100 g/4 oz black treacle
100 g/4 oz soft brown sugar
175 g/6 oz plain flour
2 teaspoons ground ginger
1 teaspoon cinnamon
1 large egg, beaten
4 tablespoons milk or skimmed milk
1 teaspoon potassium bicarbonate

Melt the butter, treacle and soft brown sugar together in a small saucepan. Mix the flour with the ginger, cinnamon and beaten egg and mix these ingredients into the butter and treacle mixture.

Warm the milk and pour it on to the potassium bicarbonate, then add this liquid to the other ingredients. Stir thoroughly. Pour the mixture into a greased 450-g/1-lb loaf tin and bake in a cool oven (150 C, 300 F, gas 2) for 1½ hours. Cool in the tin, covered with greaseproof paper, then turn out and serve sliced.

Fruit Bread

(Illustrated on page 104)

Per recipe: 220 mg sodium 3440 calories

25 g/1 oz fresh yeast *or*
15 g/$\frac{1}{2}$ oz dried yeast
150 ml/$\frac{1}{4}$ pint skimmed milk, warmed
50 ml/2 fl oz apple juice
450 g/1 lb strong white flour
5 egg yolks
175 g/6 oz caster sugar
50 g/2 oz unsalted butter, melted
150 g/5 oz mixed dried fruit

Dissolve the yeast in the warm milk and set aside. When frothy add the apple juice and stir this liquid into the flour in a bowl. Mix the egg yolks, sugar and melted butter together, then mix these into the dough. Add the fruit and knead well on a floured surface.

Set the dough aside in a warm place and allow it to rise until doubled in size. Knock back, knead lightly and form into a plait or cottage loaf.

Allow the loaf to rise again, on a greased baking tray, until doubled in size. Bake in a hot oven (225 C, 450 F, gas 8) for about 30 minutes. Cool on a wire rack.

Fruit Scones

Per recipe with skimmed or buttermilk: 90 mg sodium   1260 calories
Per recipe with whole milk: 90 mg sodium   1290 calories

100 g/4 oz wholemeal flour
100 g/4 oz plain white flour
½ teaspoon potassium bicarbonate
1 teaspoon potassium bitartrate
50 g/2 oz unsalted butter
1 tablespoon caster sugar
50 g/2 oz sultanas
100 ml/4 fl oz skimmed milk, whole milk
or buttermilk

Sift together twice, the flours, bicarbonate and bitartrate. Rub in the butter until the mixture looks like fine breadcrumbs, then stir in the sugar and sultanas. Quickly stir in the milk to give a soft but not sticky dough.

Turn the dough on to a floured board and knead until smooth. Roll out to 1-cm/½-in thickness, then cut into 5-cm/2-in rounds and place them on greased baking trays. Bake in a hot oven (240 C, 475 F, gas 9) for 7 minutes. Cool on a wire rack. **Makes 6 to 8**

Sponge Cake

Per recipe: 240 mg sodium   960 calories

3 eggs
75 g/3 oz caster sugar
65 g/2½ oz plain flour
50 g/2 oz jam

Whisk the eggs and sugar over hot, but not boiling, water until thick and pale. Remove from the heat and continue to whisk until cold. Fold in the flour using a metal spoon.

Turn the mixture into two base-lined and greased 17-cm/7-in sandwich tins and bake in a moderately hot oven (190 C, 375 F, gas 5) for 25 minutes. Remove from the tins, discard the paper base and cool on a wire rack. Sandwich the cake together with jam.

Shortbread

Per recipe metric quantities: 70 mg sodium   2910 calories
Per recipe imperial quantities: 80 mg sodium   3320 calories

This is not a low-fat, low-calorie biscuit, but a splendid melt-in-the-mouth treat for special occasions.

225 g/8 oz unsalted butter
225 g/8 oz plain flour
100 g/4 oz cornflour
100 g/4 oz icing or caster sugar

Soften the butter, then put all the ingredients in a bowl and mix thoroughly, then knead lightly. The resulting dough should look like smooth putty!

Press the biscuit mixture into a greased 20-cm/8-in square shallow tin and prick through to the base. Bake in a moderate oven (180 C, 350 F, gas 4) for about 1 hour or until the surface is golden brown.

Cool the shortbread slightly in the tin, then cut it into fingers and allow to cool completely on a wire rack. **Makes about 20**

Macaroons

(Illustrated on page 104)

Each biscuit: 10 mg sodium   80 calories

100 g/4 oz caster sugar
50 g/2 oz ground almonds
a few drops of almond essence
1 large egg white
rice paper

Sift together the sugar and almonds. Mix in the essence and egg white and beat for 5 minutes or until the mixture is stiff. Put into a piping bag fitted with a plain nozzle and pipe into rounds of about 4 cm/1½ in diameter on baking trays lined with rice paper. Allow some room for the biscuits to spread during cooking.

Bake in a moderate oven (180 C, 350 F, gas 4) for about 15 minutes. The surface should be browned and slightly cracked. Allow to become cold before removing the macaroons with the rice paper underneath. Trim the edges of the rice paper on each biscuit. **Makes 8**

Note: The mixture can also be used to make ratafias. Simply pipe tiny amounts on the rice paper and reduce the cooking time to about 5 minutes.

Gingernuts

(Illustrated on page 103)

Each biscuit: 5 mg sodium   55 calories

100 g/4 oz plain flour
½ teaspoon potassium bicarbonate
1 teaspoon Baking Powder (page 116)
¾ teaspoon ground ginger
½ teaspoon mixed spice
25 g/1 oz granulated sugar
40 g/1½ oz unsalted butter
25 g/1 oz soft brown sugar
25 g/1 oz golden syrup
25 g/1 oz black treacle

Sift together twice the flour, bicarbonate, baking powder and spices. Stir in the granulated sugar.

Melt the butter, brown sugar, golden syrup and treacle together in a small pan, then stir this mixture into the dry ingredients. Shape the mixture into about 20 small balls about the size of walnuts and space them well apart on greased baking trays. Bake in a moderately hot oven (190 C, 375 F, gas 5) for 15 minutes. Cool the gingernuts on a wire rack. **Makes about 20**

Onion Bread

Per loaf: 430 mg sodium   2300 calories

3 teaspoons dried yeast
250 ml/8 fl oz lukewarm milk
3 tablespoons oil
450 g/1 lb onions, chopped
freshly ground black pepper
1 teaspoon dried thyme
1 teaspoon rubbed sage
450 g/1 lb strong plain flour
2 teaspoons sugar
2 eggs, beaten
a little milk to glaze

Sprinkle the yeast over the milk and set aside in a warm place until the yeast has dissolved and the liquid is frothy. Heat the oil in a large frying pan, then add the onions and fry them over a medium heat until they are soft but not browned. Stir in plenty of pepper and the herbs, and set aside to cool.

Sift the flour into a bowl and add the sugar. Make a well in the middle and pour in the yeast liquid. Add the eggs and onions, then mix in the flour to make an elastic dough. Turn out on to a floured surface and knead thoroughly until smooth and not sticky. Replace the dough in the bowl, cover with cling film and leave in a warm place until doubled in size.

Quickly knead the risen dough, then shape it into one or two loaves and place them on greased baking trays. Again cover the dough with oiled cling film and leave the loaves until they have doubled in size. Brush the bread with a little milk and bake in a hot oven (220 C, 425 F, gas 7) for 15 minutes, then reduce the oven temperature to moderately hot (200 C, 400 F, gas 6) and continue to cook for a further 40 minutes.

Cool the bread on a wire rack. This bread tastes particularly good served warm. **Makes 1 large loaf or 2 small loaves**

Caraway Bread

Per loaf: 20 mg sodium   1740 calories

450 g/1 lb wholemeal flour
2 tablespoons caraway seeds
2 teaspoons dark soft brown sugar
3 teaspoons dried yeast
300 ml/½ pint lukewarm water
2 tablespoons oil

Place the flour in a bowl with the caraway seeds and sugar. Mix together well. Sprinkle the yeast over the water and leave in a warm place until the liquid is frothy. Make a well in the middle of the flour, then pour in the yeast liquid and oil. Gradually work in the flour to make a firm dough. Turn out on to a floured surface and knead thoroughly until the dough is smooth and elastic. Place the dough in a bowl, cover with cling film and leave in a warm place until it has doubled in size.

Quickly knead the risen dough, then shape it into one large or two small loaves and transfer to greased baking trays. Again cover the dough with oiled cling film and leave in a warm place until doubled in size. Brush the loaf or loaves with a little water and bake in a hot oven (220 C, 425 F, gas 7) for 15 minutes. Reduce the oven temperature to moderately hot (200 C, 400 F, gas 6) and cook for a further 30 to 40 minutes. Cool the cooked bread on a wire rack. **Makes 1 large loaf or 2 small loaves**

Walnut Bread

Per loaf: 20 mg sodium   2850 calories

450 g/1 lb wholemeal flour
175 g/6 oz walnuts, chopped
$\frac{1}{2}$ teaspoon mixed spice
2 tablespoons chopped chives
2 teaspoons sugar
3 teaspoons dried yeast
300 ml/$\frac{1}{2}$ pint lukewarm water
3 tablespoons oil

Place the flour in a large mixing bowl. Lightly roast the walnuts in a heavy-based or non-stick frying pan. There is no need to add any fat because the nuts give up their own oil. Stir the walnuts to prevent them from burning and keep the heat low. When they are slightly darker, add them to the flour and mix well. Stir in the spice, chives and sugar.

Sprinkle the yeast over the water and leave in a warm place until the yeast has dissolved and the liquid is frothy. Make a well in the middle of the flour mixture, add the yeast liquid and oil and mix in the dry ingredients to make a smooth, pliable dough. Turn out on to a floured work surface and knead thoroughly until smooth and elastic. Place the dough in a lightly oiled bowl and cover with cling film. Leave in a warm place until doubled in size.

Turn the risen dough on to a floured surface and knead lightly, then shape it into a loaf and place it on a greased baking tray. Cover with oiled cling film and leave in a warm place until doubled in size. Bake the loaf in a hot oven (220 C, 425 F, gas 7) for 15 minutes, then reduce the temperature to moderately hot (200 C, 400 F, gas 6) and bake for a further 40 minutes. Cool on a wire rack. **Makes 1 large loaf**

Index